W9-AYP-113

3-

By Rocking Chair Across Russia

Also by Alex Atkinson & Ronald Searle

★

THE BIG CITY

BY ROCKING CHAIR ACROSS AMERICA

By Rocking

ALEX ATKINSON & RONALD SEARLE

Chair Across Russia

 THE WORLD PUBLISHING COMPANY

CLEVELAND AND NEW YORK

Published by The World Publishing Company
2231 West 110th Street, Cleveland 2, Ohio

Library of Congress Catalog Card Number: 60-11457

FIRST EDITION

Certain of these pieces and their
accompanying drawings first
appeared in *Punch*

COWP
Copyright © 1960 and 1959
by Alex Atkinson and Ronald Searle.
All rights reserved. No part of this book may be reproduced
in any form without written permission from the publisher, except
for brief passages included in a review appearing in a
newspaper or magazine. Printed in the United States of America.

Contents

INTRODUCTORY NOTE

It isn't everyone who can find time to visit the Soviet Union, and even among those who never manage to go there are very few who bother to write a book about their experiences afterwards. This book is by one of the above-mentioned few—and one, moreover, who has nothing to hide. It is dedicated to those who actually *have* made the trip and have come back here with nothing but a lot of cock-and-bull stories.

Burns Night in Moscow

I HAD long wished to visit the Soyuz Sovetskikh Sotsialisticheskikh Respublik, and the only thing that ever really held me back was the difficulty of finding digs. As a matter of fact, not to put too fine a point on it, I believe that subtle obstacles were continually placed in my way. Time and again I wrote civilly enough to the Town Clerk of Zhadanov asking for a list of medium-priced boarding-houses with a view of the Sea of Azov and no restrictions about the emptying of sand out of one's turn-ups in the vestibule, and time and again all I got back was a picture postcard of Miss Zhadanov of 1931, with a message saying " The people of the Ukrainian Soviet Socialist Republic send greetings to the steel-workers of Surrey." The cancellation mark over the stamp usually said " Love your combine harvester—it is your only friend," and Miss Zhadanov was a squat matron in bathing drawers, with her hair parted in the middle and a coy scowl on her face.

It was the same with Okhotsk. I asked repeatedly for the address of a clean, respectable room on the front facing the Kamchatka peninsula, with details of day-trips to Magadan and some account of friendly casinos in the area, or picnic facilities in the foothills of the Verkhoyansk Range: but I never got a single reply, and I must say I have entertained grave doubts ever since about the efficiency of the Trans-Siberian Railway.

It is conceivable, of course, that there were sinister implications in the persistent rebuffs I received. I may at some time have been involved without knowing it in some widespread political imbroglio, an unwitting pawn in a desperate international battle of wits. My name may have been listed in heavily guarded books entitled " Known Deviationists " or " Absentee Land-lords " or even " They Liked Ike." My picture may have been carried by every Secret Policeman from Minsk to Vladivostok, and a reward of several thousand roubles offered for my capture, dead or alive. But this seems highly improbable, in view of my record. Did I not take the *Daily Worker* for six solid months, after their racing correspondent, bravely standing alone, successfully tipped Russian Hero to win the 1949 Grand National? Did I not repeatedly urge my corporal during World War II to open a second front *now*, and did he not eventually yield? Had I not kept *Das Kapital* by my bedside for years, as being cheaper than aspirin and not so fidgety as sheep? How then could I have been seriously regarded as the Terror of the Steppes?

Still, the ugly fact remains—they barred my way. They were so obstruc-tionist that I finally gave up all ideas of a seaside holiday in a secluded little Russian bay or inlet, with the balalaika music of the collectivized peasants weaving its strange, barbaric spell as I sipped my vodka beneath the striped awning outside some gay little dram shop, and the pack ice crunching in the harbour. I went to Bognor instead, and Scarborough, and once even as far as Berwick-upon-Tweed.

But the yearning persisted, and with it a feeling of guilt. Was I doing enough, I asked myself, to help in boring a hole through the Iron Curtain, to further understanding and better cultural relations between, say, the cotton-pickers of Bokhara and my grocer, a man called Richards with a son in the Young Conservatives and a growing collection of beer-mats? It was plain that I was not, and the feeling that I was letting things go from bad to worse disturbed my dreams, until at last I threw a few things into a bag, sold up my car and all but three of my Premium Bonds, and booked a passage to Moscow.

As I told reporters at the time, it was plain that *somebody* had to get over there pretty quickly and have a few heart-to-heart talks, with all cards on the table and a frank exchange of views.

" I shall not be going in any really official capacity," I said in the com-muniqué I issued on the eve of my departure, " but the members of the

Cabinet are fully aware of the purpose of my trip, and have raised no objections. They know as well as I do that if I can only get around a table with a few people like Nikolai Ilich Belayev, Pyotr Nikolayevich Pospelov, Donald Maclean, Madame Yekaterina Furtseva or Nikita S. Khrushchev, the consequences for the future could be incalculable, at the very least. "I feel I can no longer stand aside," I said, " and watch the rift widening without raising a finger. I feel that once I can get an average Russian in a corner and swap yarns with him about proportional representation, English cheddar, football pools, the Liberal revival, drip-dry shirts, purchase tax, the migration of swallows, colour television, the metric system and the unutterable foolishness of the Marxist dialectic, it will only be a matter of time before the satellite countries are given their freedom, political prisoners released, a Tory majority returned in the Presidium of the Supreme Soviet, and Uzbek families allowed at last to flock to London in their thousands for Royal Ascot."

I took with me a few symbols of our Western way of life—not so much to boast as to open the eyes of our Russian friends to the marvellous scope and variety of our culture, about which they are so woefully in the dark. Thus among other things I took a small sliced loaf, a four-bladed penknife, a platform ticket, a copy of *Blighty*, a handful of salted peanuts, a photograph of a bloated capitalist plotting to flee the country before the income-tax people can get their hands on him, some tinned rhubarb, a tape-recording of Alfred Lord

Tennyson reading "The Charge of the Light Brigade," and a selection of fourth leaders from *The Times*.

Perhaps I can best illustrate my burning determination to establish contact with these mysterious people at the earliest possible moment by outlining a conversation I had on the Russian plane not ten minutes after we took off from Copenhagen on that cold, grey afternoon in January. The air-hostess was a dark, plump girl of about forty, dressed in a lace cap, a black bombazine bodice, elastic-sided boots and a prim little jabot of white georgette. She wore no make-up and smelt of antiseptic soap and mothballs. More than once I noticed the skittish flounce of her petticoats as she passed to and fro issuing copies of yesterday's *Pravda* and humming some provocative little folk-song from Odessa. At last, when she came along at teatime to light the intricately carved candle in the ornate sconce which jutted from the inlaid mahogany bulkhead just above my head, I threw caution to the winds and seized her arm.

" Ninotchka! " I cried hoarsely.

She blushed. A middle-aged spy in an obvious disguise sat bolt upright in the seat in front, listening intently: but I was not to be put off.

" Tell me," I said, reverting to English, " which is your afternoon off? "

" Thursday," she replied, with hardly a trace of accent, drawing the knitted curtains across my little window and smoothing down my antimacassar.

" Splendid," I said. " Meet me at six outside the L.N. Tolstoy Museum in Kropotkin Street and I will show you the town. Perhaps the Bolshoi, and a couple of night-clubs to follow, eh? " And I winked.

" Sure thing," she whispered, her stainless steel teeth clashing together voluptuously.

" It was never like this on Aer Lingus," I murmured, and she withdrew to her seat at the back and threw her apron over her head.

A trivial incident, perhaps, but I think it serves to show how very narrow is the gulf that separates our two ways of life. It is also interesting to note that she didn't turn up. I stood shivering in my snow-shoes in the draught that blows up Kropotkin Street from the Moskva for an hour and a half, until two members of the M.V.D. moved me on, evidently suspecting that I was about to break into the museum and scribble all over the manuscript of *War and Peace*.

I have nothing but praise for the way Intourist looked after me. I was met at the airport at Vnukovo, hustled into a six-cylinder Zis with horsehair tip-up

seats and a built-in ormolu clock, and rushed straight to Moscow. On the way the driver, a tall man called Serge, wearing a double-breasted navy blue suit and a brown trilby hat pulled low, introduced himself as a keen follower of Wolverhampton Wanderers, and asked if I would care to visit a model safety-pin factory. " It is on our route," he confided, lowering his voice, " and I think I could get you in." When I explained that I was anxious to reach my hotel and unpack he became surly.

" You will go home to England," he said, " and you will spread poison, saying we would not permit you to see a model safety-pin factory. Then you will refuse to let China into the United Nations, and your workers will weep." Suddenly he brightened. " Do you know," he asked, " that there are twenty thousand workers reduced to begging in the streets of Chelsea alone at this time? " I said I didn't know. (To be perfectly frank, I didn't believe it.) " Such things are not reported in your newspapers," said Serge smugly, " because your leaders, William Pitt and Sir Oswald Mosley, fear an uprising. One day the truth will make itself known, and the people of Chelsea, Arsenal and West Bromwich Albion will revolt and burn down the House of Representatives."

" The House of Representatives," I said, " is in America."

" Aha," said Serge. " That's what they *tell* you."

I found something pathetic in the ignorance Serge displayed about Britain and the British way of life, and I'm afraid he was typical of many of the Muscovites I met during my stay. The strangest notions prevail among them, and although I did all I could to persuade them of the true state of things over here, I believe they prefer to revel in their blindness.

By a happy chance I arrived in Moscow on Burns Night, and as soon as I had unpacked and taken a glass of tea and a caviar sandwich I made my way to the Red Square to join the merrymaking. It was early afternoon, but already the streets were filling with revellers. It was an incredible sight. From far and near they came—from the lonely outlying villages where wolves slink through the frozen sable-farms; from semi-detached *dachas* in the exclusive suburbs; from collectives in the wild and distant wastes around Yoroslavl' and Smolensk; from the teeming tenement skyscrapers that rise like boxes of people throughout the Russian capital; from embassies and Government buildings, factories and coal-mines, labour camps and luxury suites in the Leningradskaya Hotel—a whole army of people on pleasure bent, drawn to the historic Red Square by their reverence for the humble Ayrshire

Ronald Searle MOCKBA

poet. Ox-carts groaned hub to hub along the crowded, slushy streets, crammed with gaily-ribboned peasants already drunk on home-brewed Scotch. The trolley-buses came lurching to a stop at the terminus, to disgorge fifty people at a time, all in their Sunday best, their scrupulously polished faces beaming with anticipation, their pockets bulging with oatcakes and home-made porridge. The air grew loud with snatches of song, raucous shouts, the occasional crash of a bottle being hurled on to a roof. Everywhere there was excited movement, as the multitude surged this way and that—clamouring into the dark-brown pubs (which had an extension until midnight), dancing jigs up snow-filled alleys, quarrelling, singing, praying, waving rattles. Some wore crude astrakhan sporrans, and from a far corner of the Square I heard the slow, sad wail of the pipes as someone struck up the Lament for Wee Mac-Gregor. As each Underground train arrived at the Red Square Station (change here for Gorky Street and the Sickle Line) hundreds of yelling suburbanites came pouring up the steps to add to the joyful throng. At one time I counted just under three million people in the Square, and by six o'clock there must have been even more, for at about that time the Dynamo team arrived in a coach dating back to the time of Boris Godunov, drawn by a hundred members of their Fan Club and followed by a procession of Honoured Inside Rights, second class. At a lighted upstairs window in the Kremlin, Khrushchev watched the proceedings with a merry twinkle in his eye, turning now and then to toast Mikoyan or the Minister of Culture, who stood beside him, and sometimes waving to acknowledge a more than usually fervent burst of cheering from below. Huge portraits of Burns waved crazily above the heads of the crowd, and as it grew dark great torches were lit, so that presently the whole Square was a sea of garish, dancing lights, and the proceedings took an orgiastic turn. Men, women and children moved in a close-packed mass, wolfing down handfuls of fresh haggis, passing mugs of fiery liquor from hand to hand, forming squads of a hundred and fifty at a time to dance the Gay Gordons, duelling with improvised skean-dhus in the shadow of Lenin's tomb, kissing other people's wives, swirling round in trews and ribboned bonnets. It was an unforgettable scene, and rather frightening. Faces were inflamed from drink and the flickering torchlight. A continual, unearthly rumble of noise swept up to the frosty sky, punctuated by screams, the groans of the dying, wild cries of " Hoots! " or " Good old Robbie! ", pistol shots, the clash of sabres, the neighing of terrified horses, and the war-whoops of a battalion of drunken Cossacks trying to clear a space for a

schottische.   Here and there a brown bear sniffed for scraps along the gutters, which by now were awash with melted snow and whisky.   On hastily erected rostrums impassioned professors from the Academy of Sciences vied with one another in reciting '' The Cotter's Saturday Night '' or '' Holly Willie's Prayer.''   Beside me an executive from the Central Polytechnical Library of the All-Union Society for the Dissemination of Political and Scientific Know-ledge kept bouncing up and down, shouting '' Up the Rangers! '' at the utmost power of his lungs; while from the roof of a bus stranded hopelessly in a sea of festive humanity a burly commissar in a Royal Stuart kilt (evidently a Celtic supporter) pelted him with bawbees.

Finally, as the bells of all the churches in the Kremlin struck the hour of twelve, from some tall minaret a solitary, majestic, rich bass voice boomed out the opening notes of '' Auld Lang Syne.''   It was a moment of outlandish beauty.   A hush fell over the millions in the Square: and then, with a mighty surge of sound, every single voice joined in the chorus.   The effect was awe-inspiring.   Linking arms with my neighbours, I sang as best I could, although I have never been absolutely sure of the words.   Indeed the peasant on my right gave me more than one suspicious look as I fumbled the less familiar syllables.   Then, as the last notes died away, the festivities came abruptly to an end.   The light went out in Khruschchev's window.   Plain-clothes M.V.D. men, emerging from the darkest shadows round the Square, swung their knouts meaningly.   The crowd dispersed.   In silence, with bowed heads, they shuffled away, until in all that wide space there was no living thing to be seen except myself.   An unearthly stillness brooded over the Red Square.   A ragged tam-o'-shanter, jerked across the cobbles by a fretful wind, was all the evidence that remained of the long night's boisterous revelry.

In the morning, as I looked out across the Red Square from the barred windows of my hotel, I found it hard to believe that I had not been dreaming.

The Man in the Street

I SUPPOSE the most staggering thing about Moscow is that *practically everybody you meet there wears a wrist-watch*. Make no mistake, the sooner we in the West wake up to this fact the better. During the whole of my stay I saw only *one* person carrying an hour-glass, and sundials are virtually unknown. At the same time, it must not be taken for granted that all these wrist-watches are necessarily of perfect mechanical construction or design. Far from it. Out of the two thousand and eighty-seven that I examined ("Excuse me," I would say, nudging my neighbour in the middle of the second act of *Uncle Vanya,* or beckoning to some old woman road-sweeper as I paused to light a fresh cigar, "but I wonder if I might unscrew the back off your wrist-watch for a moment?") nine hundred and twenty-two had stopped, forty-three had grit in the ratchet, just under a thousand were ten minutes fast, and one was fitted with an old bit of string instead of a strap. ("It is monstrous!" exclaimed the owner of the latter instrument, a janitor employed by the Moscow Urban District Council Communal Tractor Repair School Extra-Mural Society for the Propagation of Realist Culture and Basket

Weaving. " Already one in fifty Russian people have access to running water, yet we cannot produce a watch-strap of any consequence. Bureaucracy! Nothing but bureaucracy! First things first, that is what I say. As for this oaf, Khrushchev, I wouldn't trust him to run a cake factory." Then he clapped a hand abruptly to his mouth, pulled his cap over his eyes, and scuttled down the Metro like a rabbit.)

It is not only watches. Sugar basins are made of some strange, soft metal, and will not bounce. Glue is not sticky enough. Men's hats are a different shape from men's heads: they make your ears stick out. The telephone in my hotel room smelt of acacia on Fridays. Ladders tend to wobble. Local newspapers burn sluggishly. If you leave a kopeck in a basin of water overnight it goes rusty. Once when I jumped on a bus, the step fell off into the road. The spokes of the bicycles looked pretty flimsy to me, and middle C♯ sounded flat on most of the pianos I tried. The only inter-continental ballistic missile I saw was made partly of stiff cardboard, and would very likely blow inside out in a high wind. Soap in Moscow has a funny taste. You can put your fist through the panels of the parlour door in any worker's flat.* Little nuts keep dropping out of electric irons if you're not careful. I couldn't find a corkscrew that you put on top of the bottle and just keep on screwing until the cork comes up although I searched high and low, and one rather cheeky shop-assistant told my interpreter that such a device was no more than a bourgeois fantasy, existing only in the drug-sodden imagination of the slave-workers of President Hoover and the Duke of Bedford.

" I assure you," I said sharply, " that I have one at home."

" That is no proof," said the shop-assistant, " that it is real. And even if it were it would amount to no more than yet another attempt to drive a wedge between the U.S.S.R. and the Chinese People's Republic."

" Your tie is crooked," I said, and my interpreter took me out.

" You're going the right way," said my interpreter, " to get a punch on the nose."

" My good friend," I said, " it is only by the free and frank exchange of views that we can ever hope to iron out our differences."

We then got stuck in the revolving door, and it took the maintenance staff half an hour to set us free with hacksaws.

" My God," said the chief maintenance man, " these newfangled gadgets aren't worth the paper they're written on."

* You have to be in condition, but it can be done.

I smiled.

" In my country," I said, " revolving doors never give a moment's trouble."

" Maybe not," said the chief maintenance man. " But just you wait till they've *perfected* them."

On the other hand it should be remembered that when it comes to false hair, wooden ink-wells, sound-proofing, currant bread, half-inch cast-iron ball-bearings, jig-saw puzzle replacements, tortoiseshell earrings, ready reckoners, sand, two-way retractable flange compressors in laminated termite-proof lignite, plastic egg-separators and home-repair boot and shoe outfits, the Soviet Union is probably far ahead of its nearest rival, Moravia. As for Russian ice-cream, it comes in forty flavours, ranging from soused herring to strawberry.

The mention of ice-cream (or *morozhenoye*, to be precise) reminds me that it was in a soda-fountain that I first made contact with the Moscow beat generation.

" Hi, friend! " called a young man of about seventeen with long side-whiskers, who was lounging against the jam-tart counter as I entered. " How are the tricks with you? "

I recognized him at once as a Teddy-boy, for, quite apart from his drooping moustache, Russian Edwardian garb is distinctive. He wore a smoking-cap with a tassel, plush knee-breeches, the ribbon of the Order of Czar Nicholas I, a double-breasted brocade waistcoat, high-heeled boots and a crimson-lined cloak of ocelot trimmed with sable. As he spoke he tapped an antique snuff-box. At his feet an elk-hound menacingly bared its yellow fangs.

I bought him a coffee *morozhenoye* with chopped cherries, and we fell into conversation. He had learned to speak English at night-school, when he wasn't cutting off the girls' pigtails with a Caucasian clasp-knife, and he was most anxious to meet Marilyn Monroe, Laura La Plante and Anna May Wong, in any order. He was, he explained, a very desperate character—the spoiled son of well-to-do parents. His father was a secretary in the State Plant for the manufacture of Tram-Drivers' Gloves, and his mother was out most of the day, lolling about on divans in seedy hotels with a Manchurian diplomat who was crazy about her feet. They allowed him to read smuggled copies of *La Vie Parisienne, Harper's Bazaar* and the *Capuchin Journal* until all hours. He also ate lumps of sugar soaked in eau-de-Cologne, and he was the leader of a gang of delinquents called the Moscow Layabouts. They chalked quotations from D'Annunzio on the walls of the Spasski Tower, threw fireworks at bus queues, slashed cinema seats, chased old ladies up dark alleys, stole coats, and dropped empty cigarette packets in the public highway.

" It is partly your fault, bud," he told me, " because we are assimilating Western culture hand over the fist. Ever since Mr. Dulles was visiting here the Moscow young have been dunking doughnuts in their tea. I also know a young female who is in possession of a hula hoop. Nightly she twirls it on her neck, crying out ' I do not care! I do not care! ' Do you know Grace Moore? ''

" Unfortunately, no.''

" She appeared for the premier time at the Colonial Theatre, Boston, in *Hitchy-Coo* in 1920. This was the commencement of a new trend in Western culture, which culminated in *Rose Marie* and *Waiting for Lefty*. Have you seen these yet? ''

" Yes.''

" I dig mostly jive. I have a smuggled record of ' The Pagan Love Song ' rendered by Ramon Novarro.''

" That must be very nice.''

" It is out of this world. When I am married I do not intend to be faithful. Man alive, I will horse around like nobody's business, and dance to the music

of Debroy Somers and the Savoy Orpheans, of which I have three records. I
will criticize the régime and have a mistress. I am a regular devil, and I
don't mean maybe. If you come to my home I will show you a smuggled
photograph of King George the Fifth wearing a crown. He was a noted
capitalist who hunted birds in the Scottish tundra.''

'' Why will you criticize the régime? ''

'' I did not say I will criticize the régime.''

'' You did, distinctly.''

'' How dare you come here spreading lies and poison? I love the régime
passionately. It is only through suffering that we can hope to win through in
the end, and God knows I wish I were dead.''

Here he rested his head on a tin of wafer biscuits and sobbed piteously.
Certainly, I reflected, the Russian character is a labyrinth.

Not that this boy was typical. I found most Moscovites charming, friendly
people, with sharp teeth and unusual cuff-links. They were sometimes dark,
and sometimes fair-complexioned, and the older ones were often rather deaf.
Some, whose eyesight was obviously failing, wore glasses. But it was chiefly
by their clothes that one could tell they were Russian. For hours I would
watch them shuffling past the skyscrapers on the Kotelnit-scheskaja-Kai, like
brown lumps in the snow. The women wore coarse shawls, beige homespun
overcoats and men's boots. The men wore dark secondhand suits a size too
big, with shoddy peaked caps or fur bonnets. Now and then one more
desperate than the rest would detach himself from the throng and, approaching
me with a finger to his forelock, offer to buy my socks. In a single afternoon
I remember I got rid of an old duffel coat, two cellular undervests, a pair of
wellingtons, several hacking jackets, a camel-hair coat with a hole in one
pocket, some cork insoles (various sizes), an opera hat, a pin-stripe suit, three
pairs of cricket boots (hardly worn), a bundle of double-ended evening ties,
two plastic macs and a deerstalker hat. It was pathetic to see their eager
faces as they jostled and bargained, and I was glad that I happened to have
brought a couple of extra trunks along with me, filled to the brim with
tempting garments. (For such remote places as Ashkhabad or Severnaya
Zemlya I had a supply of beads and brightly coloured cotton piece-goods.) I
was pleased too, to receive in exchange such amusing native items as shop-
soiled transistor valves, spare parts for computers, simple slabs of caviar,
electronic devices of all kinds, collapsible jet engines, gold ornaments, small
radio telescopes, and money.

This passionate interest in Western consumer goods is widespread.   More than once, as I stopped in the street to take photographs of the frescoes on the southern portal of the Cathedral of the Ascension of the Virgin Mary, or the Ivan Veliki Bell-tower, or the apartment blocks on the Mozhaisk Chaussee, or some weeping drunk being hustled into a van by the M.V.D., I would find myself suddenly surrounded by Moscow citizens of all ages.   They seemed to sense that I was English (it may have been my shooting-stick), and after a few preliminary shouts of " We wish only for peace! " they would press close to me, fondling my camera, my umbrella, my pipe, my straw hat, my pearl-handled miniature revolver.   Little children were lifted shoulder-high to smell my hair-oil.

" Feel the quality! " they would cry, plucking at my lapels with work-worn fingers.   " Many wage-slaves must have perished under the lash producing such material! "   A babel of voices would arise, as the questions and excited exclamations echoed in the wintry air.   Those who could speak English showed off their accomplishment proudly: those who could not had to make do with Russian.

" Where is your monocle, your excellency? "

" My children crave gum! "

" Get your hair cut! "

" What about the Black and Tans? "

" I will sign your autograph book for fifty kopecks! "

,,Говорят, что в скором времени начнётся постройнии трамвая от набережной до центра города!"*

" Stop shoving at the back there! "

" We want Field-Marshal Montgomery! "

" What an exquisite complexion! "

" Enemies of Marxism, go home! "

" Kiss me, little Father! "

" Stand back, give him air! "

It was quite embarrassing at times, so great was their eagerness to see and hear and touch a living being reared in the dread shadow of democracy; but I bore it with *sangfroid*, and during my stay managed to sell four of my cameras for a little under 1500.50 roubles—a considerable gain.   All over Moscow you can see Russians gathered in circles, and at the centre of each circle there will either be an English trade union man swapping his cigarettes

---

* " It is said that the construction of a tramway line from the embankment to the centre of the town will begin shortly! "

for vodka, or an American tourist buying up at five dollars a time old ikons that have been gathering dust in attics for years. So, little by little, the Iron Curtain is being torn down, and the men in the street of East and West are coming to know one another face to face.

Apart from the Gorki Park for Culture and Recreation, where the local people gather in their thousands to ride the roller-coasters, listen to Shostakovich played by the town band, attend lectures on the Care and Maintenance of Communal Tractors, or watch mass demonstrations of arms-outward-stretch and economical muck-spreading in the open-air theatres, the best place to see the inhabitants close to is while they are out shopping. They shop in a three-storey nationally-owned department store called GUM on the Red Square, which would have been considered dowdy by Queen Victoria. The only touches of gaiety come from the whirr of the overhead wires along which the customers' change is transported in little round boxes, and the occasional busy rattle as a black-clad salesgirl manipulates her abacus. There is a smell of mothballs and musty petersham. The customers move patiently along the dim arcades, gingerly stroking here a bar of chocolate (£1 6s. 7½d.), there a tin of talcum powder (£1 10s. 0d.). They gaze with awe at the tiny, cob-webbed, dangerous-looking washing-machines (£101 17s. 0d.), the dusty loaves (five bob), the photographs of Marx or the Blagovestschenski Cathedral (1½d.), the hatpins (3/9) and the sliced boiled beetroot (all you can eat for fourpence). They point with pride to the camisole they have been saving up to buy for eighteen months, and when the armed floor-walker approaches them at the tinned salmon counter they back away murmuring " We're just looking round, sir, thank you."

I have watched them emerging from GUM at closing time, adjusting their mufflers and ear-flaps as they queue up in the slush for their suburban trolley-buses, with their parcels of dried Icelandic perch or hand-embroidered dish-cloths. I have seen them look up at the stark, bright neon signs flashing on and off against the night sky—" Save String! " and " Buy Savings Stamps! " and " Take That Grin Off Your Face! " and " Enrol Now for Moon Service! " And I have asked myself " What *is* it about the Reading Room in the British Museum? "

My Meeting With Khrushchev

QUITE a number of Russians make no secret of the fact that they belong to the Communist party. The rest (a hundred and ninety million odd) either haven't got around to joining, what with one thing and another, or are just biding their time, waiting to see which way the cat will jump.

"I reckon we ought to give it a fair trial," said a waiter in my hotel, "before we take it too seriously. Maybe it will work, maybe it won't. After all, Rome didn't fall in a day; and, as the Russian proverb says, a big bear with short legs is not necessarily any harder of hearing than a small bear with long legs if the wind is in the south."*

The results of a recent nation-wide poll, published in *Pravda* under a headline saying *Communism Here to Stay, Some Opine,* are very revealing in this connection. In answer to the question "Whom do you love?" 71 per cent said "N. Khrushchev," 23 per cent couldn't spell it, 6 per cent said "Lenin," and one fool said "Mrs. Natasha Komsoldjenskaya down the

* Some of these Russian proverbs are extremely amusing, but not all.

street." In answer to the question "If there were a General Election tomorrow how would you vote?", 20 per cent said "I sthat gun loaded?", 40 per cent said " Don't know," 15 per cent said " What the hell is a General Election? ", and the rest have mysteriously disappeared.

The fact is, of course, that the average Russian—a short, squat man with a fund of jokes, three furnished rooms, one suit, two children and a secondhand sledge, who can recite the whole of the 1945 game played in Moscow between Smyslov and Rudakovsky (the latter using the Scheveningen Variation of the Sicilian Defence) from P—K4 P—QB4 right through to R x R! Resigns—has never been particularly interested in politics, and has tended down the ages to take his rulers with something of a pinch of salt. If you look at the story of Russia you must see that on the whole he has been a pretty shrewd judge at that, because the reins have been in the hands of one bloodstained upstart after another since the dawn of history.

I soon found it more or less impossible to talk either history or world politics to the ordinary people of Moscow—partly because these subjects were superseded years ago in Russian schools by Fairy Tales for Little Folk (from *Columbus the Capitalist Pawn* to *Stalin the Cuddly Toy*) and Advanced Fairy Tales for Larger Folk (from *Clive the Indian Butcher* to *Stalin the Two-headed Fiend*); and partly because whenever I put my simple preliminary question (" Any of you chaps play Monopoly? ") the room would tend to empty in a sinister way. Drinks would be left half-finished, and small spy-holes would slide open in the panelling; there would be the unmistakable clicking of safety-catches behind innocent-looking chiffoniers, and stocky men in navy blue suits would come in and ask to see my visa. This is all due to the Soviet Penal Code, under which the Russians are forbidden to divulge certain statistical information to prying foreigners. It can be very frustrating. Nobody would tell me, for example, the date of the Treaty of Brest Litovsk, Trotsky's birthday, the time of the last train for Smolensk, or how old they were. After a few days Moscow becomes a closed book. You can't find anyone's phone number for love or money, and if you're asked to a party you're given the address in a sealed envelope, to be opened outside the city limits half an hour before zero. When you get there there is no such place, but you are met by a hooded stranger who bundles you into a plain van, blindfolds you, and takes you somewhere else. When you greet your host at last he pretends he doesn't know you, and insists not only that there never was a party but also that it took place the day before yesterday. I once asked a militiaman the way to Number 7

Suvorovsky Boulevard, and the following conversation ensued:

" There is no Suvorovsky Boulevard in Moscow. Perhaps you are thinking of Manchester."

" But I have it here in black-and-white. Suvorovsky Boulevard."

" What you have is an impudent piece of imperialist propaganda."

" I don't think so. It's a bus guide."

" Hum. Supposing there were such a place, which for the moment I emphatically deny, why would you wish to visit Number 7? "

" Because Nicolai Vasilievitch Gogol died there."

" A close relative? "

" No."

" Yet you wish to claim the body. This is strange."

" Good heavens, man, he died in 1852! "

" How do you know that? "

" It is common knowledge in England! He wrote *Dead Souls* and *Evenings on a Farm near Dikanka,* and he died in 1852! "

" It's not convincing. Gogol isn't a Moscow name. Perhaps he was one of the Verkhoyansk Gogols? "

" He was born in Sorochintsi."

" I can't place him. Did he have a drooping moustache? "

" Now look here, my good fellow, I believe you are being deliberately obstructive."

" I cannot understand your craving for Suvorovsky Boulevard. If I were you I would go to the Mariinsky Hospital for the Poor, at Number 2 Novaya Bozhedomka."

" Why? "

" Because, between ourselves, Dostoevsky was born there. Otherwise I would go to the Lenin Library. It has seventeen million books."

" Oh, very well. Direct me to the Mariinsky Hospital for the Poor."

" There is no such place. You must be mad."

Eventually, in desperation, I agreed to let him direct me to the headquarters of the All-Union Society for Cultural Relations With Foreign Countries. When I got there it turned out to be a cinema, and I saw *Broadway Melody of 1932* and a second feature called *The Steel Foundry from Outer Space.*

Happening to bump into Khrushchev a few days later at a cocktail party in one or other of the embassies* I complained rather testily to him about the

---

* One is inclined to forget details when one is caught up in the social whirl of Moscow.

Ronald Searle

secretiveness of his subjects.

" Yes, I know," he said. " I have the same trouble myself. Nobody tells me anything. 'Whatever became of Kaganovitch?' I keep asking my grocer, ' or Shepilov or Malenkov or Molotov?' And d'you think he'll answer? Not he. Ha, ha, ha. Still, as our Russian proverb says, what the eye doesn't see, the heart doesn't grieve over."

" That's an English proverb," I said.

" Oh, come, come," said Khrushchev. " You'll be telling me next you invented lampshades and custard. I suppose you want to have a long talk with me, do you, so that you can sell it to the magazines and be worshipped as a prophet?"

" Yes," I said.

" Three o'clock Friday," said Khrushchev, and moved away across the crowded room to chuck a ballerina under the chin.

These diplomatic cocktail parties and receptions, by the way, are a great feature of life in the Russian capital, and I was absolutely worn out in less than a week. Night after night the long black limousines converge on one or other of the embassies, filled with stony-faced ministers out for a jolly debauch and a chat about inter-continental ballistic missiles. Horse-drawn sleighs jingle through the Moscow dark, sending up showers of finely powdered snow. Behind the steaming horses visiting bigwigs from Afghanistan or Poland or the *Reader's Digest* huddle under rugs rehearsing their *mots* and party pieces. Inside the great houses all is warmth and glitter. Members of the Presidium mingle freely with anyone who can't conveniently escape, laughing uproariously at every chance remark and trying as hard as they can to get at least one Western journalist drunk.* Carefully prepared insults are hissed in corners. Upon the marble staircases, under the chandeliers, in the richly carpeted halls and corridors, and even in the press and bustle round the buffet table, international incidents flare up and die like fireworks. Political faces beam and sweat, the Red Army officers click their spurs at ingenues from the Moscow Art Theatre, hidden orchestras play selections from Billy Mayerl, and incensed ambassadors fly at one anothers' throats in an endless comic opera of diplomacy. At the centre of things stands Khrushchev, sipping a raspberry cordial as he pretends to listen to the gabble of interpreters. At one moment he will

* It is rumoured that their efforts met with success on one single occasion, when a *Daily Worker* man was seen to fall into a trifle. Informed opinion has it, however, that in point of fact he was pushed.

fondle some slip of a girl from the Bolshoi, complimenting her upon an *entrechat* which she thought had passed unnoticed; at another he will dig some terrified old bureaucrat from an outlying province in the ribs and accuse him of being hand-in-glove with the fanged monsters of Wall Street. Truly there is no end to the gaiety, the splendour, the romance of these diplomatic functions.

By contrast, my formal meeting with Khrushchev on that fateful Friday afternoon was stark and businesslike. It was obvious that he realized the seriousness of the occasion. He knew as well as I did precisely what was at stake.

The day was overcast, and as I walked into the Kremlin by the entrance marked:

INTERVIEWS

HEART-TO-HEART CHATS

APPOINTMENT ONLY

CLOSED SATURDAYS

I noticed that icicles hung by the wall. I was informally searched, and led into a clean waiting-room.

" There's been rather a rush today," said the guard. Then he handed me a copy of last week's *Krokodil,* poked the stove, and went away.

Three quarters of an hour later I was taken to the conference room, where Khrushchev stood with a group of advisers. He shook my hand warmly and we all sat down. He was dressed in his customary light suit and cream-coloured shirt. I wore a jacket of herring-bone tweed, an old pair of grey trousers, white shirt, club tie, brown shoes, and thick woollen underwear. Marelievsky, on Khrushchev's right, was in a dark business suit. Ajonev, on Derov's left, had a stiff white collar. Borayev, on Ajonev's right, was on Andrei Bobrezhnev's left and wore his uniform with the two top buttons of his tunic unfastened. Kirilin was on Syzhov's right,* and Kubukin sat between Petrolenski and Nicolai Bonzoi, chief accountant in the Office of Works and Dogma, who wore green knitted socks and a home-made wig. Belishova was not present, and nor were Pavel Pavlovich Lobanov, Henry R. Potemkin or Vladimir Semyenov. I did not ask why.

I sat facing the Russians across the table, with one hand palm downwards on my piece of blotting-paper and the other held in the air ready for any small

* I am not quite certain of this. It might have been Pekrebyshev—the fair one, with the mole on his wrist.

gesture that might seem appropriate. The Russians, for their part, sat facing me across the table. It seemed a fair enough arrangement.

After a long silence the interpreter asked me, politely but meaningly, whether I realized it was very nearly teatime. I then read a prepared statement of thirty-odd pages, and Khrushchev said he couldn't make head or tail of it.

" It seemed clear enough to me," said the interpreter. " He says there's tension in the world."

" Tension be damned," said Khrushchev. He pointed a chubby finger in my direction. " If you'd stop sending children-in-arms up chimneys," he said, " you might be in a position to talk."

" I don't send anybody up chimneys," I said, knowing full well that the Russians admire courage, and even recklessness, in debate.

" I don't give a hang *who* sends them," said Khrushchev. " You get them down, that's all I'm saying! Get them down, and quick, or U.N.O. will hear about it, don't you fret! "

" We seem to have reached a deadlock," I said.

" That's not important," said Khrushchev, rising jovially. " The important thing is that we have aired our differences. Good day. If you will call at the porter's lodge on the way out he will give you back your wallet, keys and personal belongings. Glossy photographs of myself stepping out of an aeroplane are also available, price forty kopecks."

" Good day, gentlemen," I said.

It was exactly seventeen minutes to five. As I emerged into the Red Square a small crowd of bystanders, who had been waiting in the bitter wind to cheer my departure, gathered eagerly around the car, reaching out to touch me, so that they might have something to tell their grand-children.

A Trip to The Caucasus

WHICHEVER way you look at it, the U.S.S.R. extends nearly half-way round the world. At one end (on the right-hand side) it is only fifty-six miles from the U.S.A., and at the other end it borders on Czechoslovakia, a free and independent republic. It has been said that you could jump on a horse and ride for three solid months without reaching the edge of Russia, and I met a man in Tashkent, the younger son of a People's Professor of Advanced Studies in Soil Erosion and Artesian Well Culture, who had actually made the experiment. He should have stayed at home. His horse fell down in a heap towards the end of the first fortnight, absolutely dog tired, and he hadn't the remotest idea where he was. To make matters worse it was pouring with rain. It transpired that he had turned left by mistake at Grozny and was only a stone's-throw from Saudi Arabia. He sold the horse to a commercial traveller in Baghdad, and it took him the best part of a year to get back home, picking up a precarious living by singing his native Uzbek folk-songs to cinema queues and encampments of nomad Afghan tribes-men, who threw old dates at him.

"You ought to have your head examined," said his father. "A grown man like you should have known it was just an old wives' tale."

In all this vast expanse of country there isn't a single golf course—or if there is I didn't see it, and I travelled pretty extensively, I can tell you. I told the Intourist people in Moscow one day that I was thinking of pushing off for a while to poke about in the bush and see how the other half of the world was getting on. I quickly learned that although Russia is enormous it tends to shrink in a mysterious way as soon as a foreign tourist threatens to go and have a look at it. I assure you it is no use getting a map out on the counter in the Intourist office and thinking you can just start jabbing your finger at random and asking for bus tickets. On Wednesdays and Fridays, to take a typical instance, you can't go to Azerbaijan S.S.R. Again, the eastern end of Kazakh S.S.R. is open only to accredited Chinese tourists with a letter of recommendation from Chou En-lai. Nobody has seen head or tail of Samarkand since 1950, and Norilsk is surrounded by barbed wire.

"Why not go to Wrangel Island?" suggested Tamara, a roguish Intourist chauffeuse with raven hair and two decorations for netball. "You could be there in eighty days."

"But it says here it's mostly uninhabited tundra," I said, "surrounded by floating pack ice."

"Wherever you went the sun would shine," said Tamara, fluttering her eyelashes. "And you could take a hot-water bottle just in case. Let me come with you, and I will be your slave."

"Don't be facetious," I said. "You're showing a flagrant disregard for the principles of socialist realism."

"I'll bet you say that to all the girls," said Tamara. "May I call you Alexei?"

"No, you may not. I want to go to Tannu Tuva."

"Tannu Tuva is on the border of Manchuria and therefore forbidden. Try again next month."

"I see what it is," I said. "You're making fiendish weapons in all these places. Forced labour is working day and night in chain-gangs, rigging up rockets aimed straight at the soft underbelly of Staffordshire and the industrial heart of Milwaukee. One of these days, after a night of orgy and debauch, some mad underling in the Kremlin is going to press a button. There'll be a sinister whooshing noise in a clearing on the wooded slopes of the Urals, and that'll be the end of St. Anne's-on-Sea. I know your little game,'' I said. '' You're just trying to make things awkward, crossing places off your map as though they were dishes on a menu. Pah! We don't behave like this to tourists in England. They can go strolling through the streets of Oldham or King's Lynn at any time they wish, without so much as a by your leave. And d'you know why? Because we have nothing to hide, that's why! ''

'' I know,'' said Tamara. '' And don't you just wish you had! ''

'' Look here,'' I said, '' give me a third monthly return to Birobidzhan, and let's have no more nonsense.''

'' I believe you're just a beautiful spy,'' said Tamara.

Eventually I settled for a round trip to the Caucasus, a mountain region in the south which includes a place called Georgia where they grow peaches. It was not an easy journey. The train left Kursk Station at 7.30 p.m., and I boarded it just in time, accompanied by my Intourist entourage. There were first of all four interpreters in very thick overcoats. There was a chauffeur with a peaked cap. There was the chauffeur's bodyguard. There was the wife of the Tartar interpreter, sneaking a ride to visit her ailing mother on a Transcaucasian tobacco plantation. There were two guides who couldn't speak English, a licensed hunter in case we were attacked by aurochs, wolves, lynxes or panthers (which seemed extremely likely), a woman to do the washing and ironing, her two children, a small dog called Tanya, a minor official from the Ministry of Folk-lore and Cultural Misunderstanding, three pack-mules, a Mr. Vhagorsk whose job it was to keep close at my heels and wait for me to make a false move, an Azerbaijan entertainer to while away any tedious nights we might have to spend in snowdrifts by juggling with flaming swords and singing the good old songs, the Moscow representative of the Armenian Public Relations Department, the fashion editress of *Trud,* and a man to carry the bags.

Day after day the train rolled through the flat, endless countryside, and I must say it soon began to get rather stuffy in our compartment. The hunter kept wanting the window open on account of the chauffeur, who smoked a pipe incessantly, but Mr. Vhagorsk wouldn't hear of it, for security reasons. The washerwoman's children kept finding rabbits and geese up the sleeves of the Azerbaijan entertainer's gown, and two of the interpreters played a noisy game of beggar-my-neighbour from morning to night. The man from the Ministry droned on about the differences between Tchetchens, Lesghians, Kabards, Tartars, Georgians and Mingrelians, and how they all loved Mr. Khrushchev dearly for allowing them independence under his thumb. To add to the noise and general confusion, the train loudspeaker kept blaring and chattering away, relaying music by Khatchaturian, excerpts from *Dombey and Son,* classified football results, and exhortations to wash behind the ears, eat less bread, and be kind to the elderly.

During the hours of daylight I would sit at the window if I could get the dog Tanya out of the way and watch the Russian landscape gliding past—a truly fascinating kaleidoscope comprising tiny thatched cottages, dense forests,

herds of buffalo, electric power-stations, villagers in gay turbans or *vodnoy rubashke** tilling the soil with pointed sticks, wind mills, blast furnaces, workers' convalescent homes and wide plains of grassland stretching as far as the eye could see.   At Belogorod, at the edge of the Ukraine, we all got out on to the platform to stretch our legs and were quickly surrounded by vendors of Turkish delight, pickled onions, whole roast Muscovy ducks, bubble-gum, native gourds, cheese sandwiches and unfermented grape-juice.   A newspaper-seller strolled up and down with a cart full of papers and magazines, calling out " *Izvestia! Literaturnaya Gazeta! Red Star! TV Fun! Soviet Woman! Komsomolskaya Pravda! Ogonyok!* Yesterday's *Evening Moscow!* " Approaching me, he felt under his cart, winked, and produced a well-thumbed black market copy of *Harper's Bazaar* containing a preview of the spring fashions for 1934, for which he asked three pounds ten shillings at par, or a pair of English shoes and a copy of *Dr. Zhivago.*   I refused this, and chose the current *Ogonyok,* the Soviet answer to *Life,* which entertained me all the way to Kharkov with its photographs of Honoured Lady Weight-Lifters of the R.S.F.S.R., a coloured six-page supplement about love and laughter in a champion cement works, and a five-thousand-word article on the care and maintenance of a communal cesspool, with diagrams.

" You like our magazines? " inquired one of the interpreters, as he finished translating for me an account of a stormy meeting of the Leningrad Bus Workers' Committee for Cultural Recreation and Home Dressmaking.

" They are unique," I replied.

He beamed.   " To-morrow I will read to you the jokes from *Krokodil.* You like *Krokodil?* "

" It is not as good as it was," I said.

We rumbled through Kharkov, dawdled into Rostov, crossed the Don, and chugged along the coast of the Black Sea, past beaches where workers on holiday lazed in the sun in woollen bathing-costumes, reading improving books or (so the guide told me) engaging in educational quizzes to keep their minds clear for their return to factory bench or workshop floor.   At last we reached the Caucasus range, and as we climbed painfully through the rugged peaks, with Mount Ararat on our right and the rock where Prometheus came to grief somewhere over on the left, I was able to look down on timeless hamlets nestling in green folds of the hills, with Circassian dancers shooting out their legs in the vigorous *vprisyadku* dance on village greens in the cool of the

* Wearing nothing but a shirt.

evening, their wild cries echoing in the valleys like the shunting of distant goods wagons, the polished leather of their Russian boots glinting in the last rays of the sun.   And so we came to Tiflis.*

The Caucasus is like another world after the formal, glum Edwardian sophistication of Moscow.   I felt quite out of place wearing a lounge suit in Tiflis.   Here all was bustle and barbaric splendour, with sabres clashing, bells tinkling, and wild horses pounding about in all directions.   The very songs in the pubs were different.   Whereas at closing-time in Gorky Street you might see some gloomy artisan come stumbling out of an ale-house singing:

> Natasha the nut and bolt sorter with dimples
> Is loved by all on the night-shift;
> All men on the afternoon-shift too love Natasha;
> How unfortunate then am I
> Who love her best of all, hey ho,
> For I am on the morning-shift
> And can get neither a transfer to the afternoon-shift
> Nor a transfer to the night-shift, hey ho.
> CHORUS
> Still I do not complain to my foreman,
> That good wise man.
> For when productivity has risen sufficiently
> It is reasonable to suppose that Natasha will accept me
> If I ask her,

or some other Westernized popular song, here in the heart of the Caucasus the songs are hearty, robust epics of a bygone age.   Bands of richly adorned horsemen in Turkish trousers, brilliantly embroidered shirts and socks, fur hats and long tasselled gowns go clattering up and down the dusty alleys singing of kings who married nightingales.   Uzbeki villagers in their little round berets throng the main streets of Tiflis, swigging *kumiss*† from crude cups and obviously having about as much in common with Lenin, Trotsky, Zinoviev, or Kamenev, as J. Stalin had with Henry VIII.

Here, I thought, was a great wonder indeed.   Was it possible, I asked the members of my entourage, to believe that these fierce moustachioed tribesmen in their long *cherkeskas*‡, cooking *shashlik* on their daggers over open fires, were

---

* Tbilisi.
† Fermented mare's milk.
‡ Skirts, as far as I know.

47

fully paid-up members of the U.S.S.R.? And these flat-faced Buryat Mongols from the hills? Would blast-furnaces and hydro-electric plants and co-operative ball-point pen factories ever really rise among these sleepy villages, where a homeless peasant will dig a rectangular hole in the ground four feet deep, line it with logs, pull the roof on over his head, light his pipe, and not give a tinker's cuss?

" It is hard for you to understand," said the fashion editress of *Trud,* " but there is a Russian proverb which says ' It is surprising what a little encouragement will do, and failing that some other means must be devised '."

But I was not convinced. There are thousands of people in the Caucasus who cannot understand a word of Russian. There are even tribes descended from the Crusaders who go about their daily tasks in suits of armour, and nobody's going to teach *them* the finer points of dialectical materialism in a hurry, let alone how to take a motor-bike and sidecar to bits and put it back without spilling anything. I tell you plainly, the people I saw in Tiflis are no more like the people of Moscow or Leningrad than the people of Moscow or Leningrad are like the shoppers in Reading on a Saturday morning, ambling along Castle Street in their hunting pink and singing " Summer is i-cumen in " as they stack their week-end joints of venison into the backs of their station-wagons. Nobody was more surprised than Karl Marx when the Russians, of all people, decided to give a few of his notions a trial; and after my trip I felt bound to write an urgent note to the Chairman of the Presidium of the Supreme Soviet, advising him to change his mind while there was still time. For some reason this note does not appear to have been delivered. But whatever happens in the future, no one can say I didn't warn them.

The Past and The Present

IT goes without saying that nobody who spends as long as I did studying the U.S.S.R. can avoid being regarded as an authority on the place in the end. It can be very tiresome, what with all the parties, and the lectures, and the television appearances, and the total strangers stopping one in the street to say '' I hope you won't mind me stopping you in the street, but I did want to hear from your own lips whether there's going to be a war ''; but it's inevitable, and I knew before I went that a man in my position must shoulder his responsibilities. It was for this reason that I took care during my stay to make myself thoroughly acquainted not only with Russia's topography, domestic politics, agricultural statistics, secret defences, principal exports, national character, military might, cultural patterns, prison-reform programme, attitude to the common cold and postal arrangements over the Christmas holiday, but also with its history. To many people in the West this great country suddenly and inexplicably sprang into existence, fully grown, in the early 'twenties, and insinuated itself into the international scene by sending men with beards and slouch hats to prowl about the darkened streets of English suburbs with bombs under their cloaks. Some people have an earlier, mistier recollection of there having been a Russia a few years before this, in which whole families sat around in twilit gardens worrying about sea-gulls, or quietly shooting themselves, or engaging in the gentle art of soliloquy, or threatening to go to Moscow, or simply sobbing their hearts out.   But on the whole a woolly ignorance prevails.   I am therefore glad to be able to set before you now an account of what went on in Russia after the mammoths and the sabre-toothed tigers had beat it into the woods and left man to do his worst.   This account I pieced together painstakingly—from scraps of conversation overheard in bars, from a few casual words dropped by a University student in Balashov, from museums, from old men on park benches, and from the shrewd grilling of official guides from Smolensk to Vladivostok.

History, it seems, dawned rather late in Russia, chiefly on account of the weather.   Eventually, however, a lot of Scythians wandered in from Asia, cursing through the swamps and forests, and the stage was set for serfdom, Rasputin, revolt, and the dramatic flight of Burgess and Maclean.   The Scythians were an uncultured crowd, even for 8 B.C., and the Slavs, who followed them in, were not much better.   An interesting point about these Slavs is that nobody seems to know quite where they came from in the first place.   It is my own belief, based on a day's digging in the vicinity of Dnepropetrovsk and a chat with a man in the second-class buffet on Kuibyshev station, that they were there all the time, hiding.   Next came the Vikings, who sailed all over the place in their clumsy great boats and founded a dynasty at Novgorod in 862, with a man called Rurik in charge.   In the meantime southern Russia kept being invaded by hordes.   These mostly consisted of hairy men with no manners, who galloped about on shaggy horses not giving a tuppenny damn for anyone.   They included Huns, Avars, Goths, and a sprinkling of Khazars.   Finally, in 1237, Ghengis Khan's nephew sent his Tartars in to conquer what was left, and history really got started.   A man called Ivan, a descendant of Rurik, defeated the Tartars at a splendid battle in which both sides fled in terror simultaneously, and he became the first of the Czars.   He, or someone very like him, thought up the idea of having serfs, and they turned out to be a great success.   His wife Sophia, a Greek, brought in some Italian architects to build the Moscow Kremlin, which looks as though it was carved out of mint humbugs.   His grandson, Ivan the Terrible, distinguished himself when he was only thirteen by having his chief adviser torn to bits by savage dogs, and later chose, from a crowd of fifteen hundred virgins specially selected from all over Russia, a girl called Romanov to be his bride, thus sowing the seeds for the plot of *Anastasia*.   He also invented the secret police, and when he eventually became a monk and changed his name to Jonah many people thought it was the least he could have done, all things considered.   The Romanovs stepped in in 1613, when Ivan's grand-nephew Michael took the throne.   Peter the Great, a seven-foot dentist, reigned from 1689 to 1725, had his son tortured to death and was succeeded by his widow, a Lithuanian servant girl named Martha Skavronska who was naturally known as Catherine I.   There were three more ladies after that—Anna, Elizabeth, and Catherine the Great, a German, who gave land and serfs away right, left and centre to her multitudinous lovers and didn't look remotely like Marlene Dietrich.*   Her son Paul tried to do something about making life easier for the serfs.†   Next came three Alexanders, two Nicholases, and the October Revolution of November 1917.   There are now no serfs, officially, and everyone is happy.   All that remains is to do something about the plumbing.

One morning, soon after my return to Moscow from my exploration of the Caucasus, I presented myself at the Intourist office and said I would like to go to Leningrad to see the Hermitage Museum.   " Also Kiev," I said, " if it's not too much trouble, and some of these Virgin Lands I've heard so much about."

" My God," said the round-faced girl behind the counter, with flaxen plaits coiled high on her head and the shoulders of a born discus thrower, " you're a glutton for punishment, aren't you? "

" Come along, now," I said, " I haven't got all day.   Here are my finger-prints, passport, potted biography and last school report.   Here are my clearance papers from the Ministry of Spies, two recent glossy photographs, five shillings deposit, my gun permit, and certificates of vaccination against frostbite and beri beri.   Here is a letter of introduction from a prominent churchman.   Here are my identity card, my clothing coupons, an application form for luncheon vouchers, my entry permit, my horoscope, my visa, my home address, my medical history, a current monthly season ticket between Wandsworth Common and Victoria, and eight refills of genuine English kiss-proof lipstick, in the new, passionate tangerine shade.   You Too Can Drive Men Utterly Crazy."

" I'll settle for the lipstick.   You'd better shove all that other junk back in your sponge-bag."   She clapped her hands, and a saturnine man with a thick

---

* To this day nobody in Russia can understand why Marie Dressler didn't get the part.
† He was out of his mind.

Kazakh accent came through a sliding panel, wearing a liftman's uniform. (All uniforms in Russia are liftmen's uniforms, and this can lead to untold pandemonium, as when I dragged a drab-looking fellow into what I thought was a lift on the ground floor of GUM and asked him curtly for lampshades and soft furnishing, only to find I was in the ladies' powder-room with an Aeroflot navigator second-class in his walking-out clothes.) "Ivan, this gentleman wants to go to Kiev, Leningrad and the Virgin Lands," said the Intourist lady. "Please detail two secret policemen to dog his footsteps, and make the usual interminably protracted arrangements for the trip."

"Rely on me, Comrade Anna," said Ivan, and ushered me into a cell for interrogation.

"Look here," I said, "where's Tamara? I never have all this trouble with Tamara."

"I don't doubt that for a moment," said Ivan, sitting at a bare table and loosening his cartridge-belt. "Tamara has been removed to our branch office at Khabarovsk on the Manchurian frontier, for uncultured behaviour."

"What is uncultured behaviour, may I ask?"

"Flirting. Now then. Name in full?"

Three days later (a record) I was in Kiev, six hundred and twenty-eight miles south-west of Moscow, on the right bank of the Dnieper, being shown round an Anti-Tank Gun Manufacturing and Assembly Plant with a party of Hungarian school-children. Kiev is a lively city by comparison with Moscow, and has some of the most beautiful churches in the world. "Do you not find these churches something of an embarrassment?" I asked my guide as we stood outside St. Andrew's. "Not at all," he replied. "They keep the older folk amused, and many tourists come to see the mosaics. Next question, please." There are also many trees, ample accommodation for bathing in the icy Dnieper, and five thousand future nuclear physicists in the Shevcheko University, going at it like beavers.

Since Kiev is in the Ukraine, I took the opportunity to see some of the famous "black earth" country. It was most impressive. The wheat here grows so tall that hardly a week passes without some party of meddling Inspectors from Moscow getting lost in it. This amuses the Ukrainians, who are a merry, borsch-guzzling crowd on the whole, and have never thought much of Russians anyway. "They come here," I was told, "to pry about with tape-measures and suchlike. I have seen a *droshky* full of them, with a coachman and a team of horses and luggage and all, drive straight into a wheat

field and get lost to sight in the twinkling of an eye. When it's time for the combine harvesters to get to work, you'd be surprised at the things they find in that wheat. One year we came across a bus, a 23a double-decker. Another time we found a whole string quartet that had been sent to entertain the workers on a collective farm in the district. They'd been living for three weeks on rabbits and field-mice, and the cellist had grown a beard.''

Oh, a very merry lot, the Ukrainians. I was sorry to leave them, but time was short and Leningrad was over six hundred miles away, to the north. It was foggy when I got there, and bitterly cold. As I stepped down from the Red Arrow Express, which goes non-stop from Moscow to Leningrad in a dead straight line and must send the engine-drivers mad with boredom, I was met by a guide in a pin-stripe suit and a Homburg hat (Leningrad is as near to being Westernized as any Russian city can be without juke-boxes) who escorted me to a waiting Zim and told me that we had to see forty-seven museums, one thousand seven hundred libraries, Lenin's armoured car, the Pavlov Institute, the skeleton of the largest prehistoric elephant in the world, the Hermitage, and Kazan Cathedral, which is now the Museum of the History of Religion and contains replicas of torture chambers from the Spanish Inquisition. I said I'd rather have a cup of cocoa.

Two days later, when I'd thawed a little, I went to the Hermitage and saw two Leonardo da Vincis, dozens of Picassos, twenty-five Rembrandts, scores of Rubenses, and *thousands* of French Impressionists.

'' Great heavens! '' I cried, as we stumbled into one of the fifteen hundred rooms and found ourselves knee-deep in unframed Matisses, Monets, Manets, and Cézannes. '' This is incredible! ''

'' I know,'' said my guide apologetically, '' but at least we try to keep them out of sight as far as possible. To-morrow I will show you some really *artistic* works. Do you know Ioganson's ' At An Old Urals Plant,' or Talevich's ' Tea Break In a Kharkov Truck Factory '? ''

'' Get me out of here,'' I said weakly. '' All this culture is killing me. It is high time I went to the Virgin Lands.''

To The Virgin Lands

I HAVE decided not to reveal here the identity of the Moscow official of the Ministry of Hedging and Frustration who received my application for a Travel Permit and actually made it possible for me to pay a visit (strictly against regulations existing at that time) to a Virgin Land. Suffice it to say that he was, as luck would have it, one of the leading members of an underground movement bitterly opposed to the Soviet system, who are working day and night, by devious means, to overthrow the régime. From small beginnings, over the past twenty years this movement has grown in strength, until to-day it numbers no less than five—four highly trained men and a young lady from Riga: and slowly but surely they are sowing the seeds for a Conservative revolution, with the ultimate aim of restoring the monarchy and introducing staggered unemployment, no free milk in schools, tax relief for landlords, and the inalienable right of any citizen to ruin his neighbour in free and healthy competition. Whenever you hear of a mysterious ten-minute hold-up on the Moscow Metro during the rush hour, or a misprint in *Trud,* or the point-blank refusal of a Russian rhesus monkey to send back any relevant data to speak of from outer space, or a lightning strike of riveters' mates in the atomic submarine yards at Zhdanov, you may be sure that the Movement has been at work.

"We regard ourselves as little more than guerrillas at present," this man told me (he was a thin chap with weak eyes, and the moths had been at his hat); "but the day is not far distant now when we will be in a position to nominate a candidate to stand as an Independent National-Liberal at the elections. It will be a beginning. After that we shall see what we shall see."

He said that the members of the Movement do not address one another as Comrade, but as Mate, or Love, or Sport, or Bud, in the Western fashion. They have a secret arms dump on the outskirts of the city, consisting of twenty-seven rounds of live ammunition. "All we need now," the man said, "is a gun to fit it."

Although I had no wish to presume to meddle in the internal affairs of a friendly foreign power, it seemed to me only polite to wish him luck. "After all," I said, "these things tend to go in cycles. Who knows—one day you may find yourself being issued with serfs."

The permit he gave me entitled me to travel tourist class to a place called Yomsof and back. I couldn't find it in my *Baedeker,* which didn't surprise me when I learned that until the previous month it had been no more than a clearing in the tundra. It was apparently chosen as the latest Virgin Land at a meeting of the Co-operative Planning and Reclamation Sub-Committee of the Department of Cultural Engineering and Manpower Dispersal, the chairman simply jabbing a pin at random into a large-scale map of Siberia and saying "Let's send some of the blighters here to grow pineapples."

The scene at the station, as the great Virgin Lands Express stood getting up steam for its long journey to the Unknown, was lively in the extreme. The platform was crowded with Soviet citizens from all over the Union—Uzbeks from Samarkand with gold teeth and baggy trousers, Kazakhs from Alma-Ata in velvet pantaloons, Armenian shoemakers, Georgian carpet-weavers, Russian electronic-computer operators, Latvian glass-blowers, Estonian displaced persons, Lithuanian tree-fellers, Tadzhik cotton-spinners, Moldavian fruit-pickers, Azerbaijanian sword-swallowers, Kirghizian tractor-drivers, and a clerk from East Berlin. Good-byes were being said in a hundred different tongues. Old women were weeping, old men were asking the porters if this was the right train. Notice-boards stood at intervals, bearing such chalked instructions as " Assembly Point for Sheet-Metal Workers' Party from Krasnoyarsk," " Have Your Tickets Ready," " Secret Police Report Here," " Vaccination Centre," " Khrushchev Is Very Nice," " Queue For Rations," or " Will Mrs. Kuzmufin Please Go To The Stationmaster's Office? " Most of the children had flags inscribed " It is better to die for one's country in the frozen north than to hang around street corners in Leningrad," and I noticed one happy party of Letts, chained together at the ankles, singing some rousing pioneer chorus as they were stuffed into a steel-lined truck next to the guard's van by a jolly militiaman. All was bustle and clatter and confusion. The hiss and roar of steam, the rattle of porters' wagons, the yelping of dogs, the wailing of wives and sweethearts, the tramp of marching men, the shrilling of police whistles, the thud of rifle butts on astrakhan caps, the gabble of a thousand conversations, the crash of empty vodka bottles being tossed on to the tracks, the strident cries of the hot pie vendors and the powerful blare and bray of the Moscow Fire Brigade (South-Eastern Section) Silver Prize Band playing a pirated selection from *My Fair Lady* outside the buffet, all combined to make the occasion deafeningly memorable. As the time for departure grew near the Virgin Lands Express, standing like some gigantic covered wagon, became packed more and more tightly with brave adventurers, setting out on a journey that would carry them thousands of miles from their homes, far into the icy waste-lands, the untrodden wilder-nesses of the north, to dig and sweat for the greater glory of the U.S.S.R. and a small percentage of the profits.

Last farewells were still being anxiously babbled as the train began to hiss and thunder slowly out of the station.

" Take good care of Grandpa's leg! "

" Be sure that Pavel gets his iron tonic! "

" Good-bye, dearest twin sister! "

" Send back money, for the love of heaven! "

" Look for the grave of poor Ivan Ivanovitch! "

" Mother, I do not wish to go! "

" But of *course* I will be faithful to you, Anushka, in Franz Josef land! "

" My son, my son, you did not pack your woollen underpants! "

And so another train-load of volunteers left Moscow; and as the great express began to eat up the miles across the endless plain, the brave youngsters leaned from the windows, singing their pioneer songs and waving derisively to the village stay-at-homes, lolling in the sun waiting for the pubs to open.

The older people huddled together in silence, waiting for someone to bring them cups of tea, their weeping unheard in the train's monotonous clamour.

On the third day I fell into conversation with a young student in the dining-car. Once I had convinced him that I was not one of the nine hundred *Life* reporters known to be in the area trying to smuggle themselves into a Virgin Land on the offchance of getting a blurred photo of volunteers being shot down like dogs for complaining about weevils in the bread, he spoke quite freely about his hopes for the future, enlivening his talk with a wealth of statistical information which I surreptitiously wrote down on the back of a cigarette packet to sell to the highest bidder on my return to the West.

"In three years' time," he said, "my country will be producing one and a half times as many plastic handbags *per capita* as the U.S.A., with or without tin clasps. In one year's time our output of dried acacia leaves will have trebled, and the price of our raspberry jam will have gone down by the equivalent of a trifle under fourpence a pound. In fifty years' time every man, woman and child in the U.S.S.R. will have two bicycles."

"This must make you very happy," I said.

"There is no time to be happy," said the youth, "but I must acknowledge that I experience a feeling of exhilaration when I remember that by unselfishly setting out to make a new life in the Virgin Lands I am playing a noble part in furthering the economic expansion of the motherland."

"Haven't I seen you somewhere on a recruiting poster?" I asked.

"You have much to learn from us," said the youth. "Out of the barren deserts we are bringing forth Cellophane-wrapped jam-tarts and laminated aluminium double-ended universal swivel-joints with two-way auxiliary angle-brackets. What are you doing? You are watching *I Love Lucy* and licking the boots of your bloated shareholders."

"You have spies everywhere," I said, "that's very plain to see."

"You English lack imagination, initiative and the will to prosper by expansion," he said. "Otherwise you would long ago have opened up knitting-needle works in the abandoned solitudes that stretch northwards from Knightsbridge to the Bayswater Road. Why does not your government permit your workless millions to make the long trek into the wild desolation of the uncharted territory between Stratford-upon-Avon and Crewe and start a new life for themselves planting sisal? What has become of your much-vaunted spirit of adventure? Where are your Sir Roger Drakes and your Sir Francis Casements? You have been outstripped, tovarich, because you have turned into a nation of pasty-faced stay-at-homes. Your young men do nothing but play at cricket and *chemin-de-fer,* and stab one another with flick knives. Your young women have no aim but to develop into flat-chested mannequins with bony red ankles, so that they may be chosen as concubines by drug-sodden, pimply international playboys and die of an overdose of barbiturates in flower-decked suites in the luxury hotels of Europe. Are you going to deny that they would be better off from every point of view chopping up pig swill on some State farm in Middlesex, under proper supervision? ''

'' Lie down, lad,'' I said, '' and try to get a bit of sleep. Foam is beginning to come out of the corners of your mouth.''

'' It is only by a free and frank exchange of opinions that we can ever hope to—''

'' Yes,'' I said, '' I know. And there are times when I wonder if it's worth it.''

So the great express rolled on by day and by night, through swamp and grassland, igneous and metamorphic rocks, old red sandstone, forest and woodland, peat bogs, limestone grits, turnip fields, clay lowlands, minor scarps of ironstone, heathland, moorland and rough pasture, rugged upland shale, pre-Cambrian volcanic rocks, urban districts, folds of tertiary basalt, orchard and nursery gardens, escarpments of coal-bearing strata, alpine meadows, temperate mixed forests, cool coniferous deserts, savanna, alluvial deposits, controlled and uncontrolled level-crossings, floating ice-caps and other features of absorbing geological, palæontological, dendrological, ichthyological and demographological interest; and day and night the pioneers munched their black bread, snored, became betrothed, fought, sang, jumped from carriage windows with shrill cries, read tea-cups, knitted mittens, shaved in lukewarm water, and told their life stories over and over again to the people sitting opposite, who wanted to get on with the crossword.

And at last, shortly before a quarter to three one bleak Thursday afternoon, we came to a stop at Yomsof Station, which consisted of two planks in the snow and a dark-brown corrugated-iron shed marked '' Keep Out.'' A chill wind was blowing. As we clambered painfully down from the train to be hustled into three ranks by a sergeant of militia, sleet came swirling in from the north-east, so that we had to keep our eyes shut. After a roll-call we were marched off into the grey, sodden wilderness towards Yomsof itself, which lay hidden in a valley some eight miles from the station. I can still hear the crunch and slur of our boots as we moved in a long, snaking line, three abreast, heads down into the biting wind with our luggage on our backs. Somewhere in the rear a concertina played an old, sad folk song.* Apart from that the silence was broken only by one of the older people occasionally blowing his nose, or falling with an exclamation of surprise into a slush-filled pot-hole.

Yomsof! Shall I ever forget my first sight of that romantic township, nestling against the timeless, lichen-covered crags! Log houses stood in rows along the main street, and along the other street there were gay log cinemas, log super-markets, a log post-office, log pit-head baths, a log jail, log livery stables, log dram shops and an ornate log puppet theatre. In every direction tracks led off through the snow, and as I stood in the market-place in the fading light late that afternoon, beside the communal log drinking-fountain, I watched the sun-bronzed workers tramping back from field and factory—singing, always singing—their faces aglow with hope and faith and pride in the future of abundant prosperity they were building for their motherland. Here were the brawny iron-founders and steel-workers, trudging home from secret blast-furnaces and strip mills in the nearby range of foothills; here were reindeer breeders—strong, hairy fellows with old newspapers stuck in their boots for extra warmth; here were the women, pale with fatigue but smiling after a hard day planting daffodil bulbs and spinach; here were the lads with spades, whose job it was to scrape away the snow so that the tractors could sow spring wheat or barley; here came the merry hop-pickers, fun-loving gipsies from far-off Bukhara and nomads from the mysterious regions of Turkmenistan, all garlanded with leaves and hungry for their supper of tinned sardines and cabbage; and the pottery workers hot from their primitive kilns, the shipbuilders from the icy lake, the sewing-machine makers, the designers of ballet shoes, the uranium diggers under heavy guard, the shepherds, harvesters, cowhands, planters of pomegranates, packers of meat paste and a flock of chattering girls from the vinegar factory.

Who can doubt, I asked myself, that something will come of all this? Can we in the West afford to ignore the threat of such feverish activity in the Russian wastelands? Is Harlow New Town really a sufficient answer? The more I saw of the people of Yomsof at work and play during the few days of my stay among them, the more I became convinced of their willingness to endure privations and discomforts of all sorts for the ultimate common good,

* As far as I can recollect, it was *Ramona*.

provided there is no other way out. Could we of the West say the same? And whatever the answer to that question, or to three others which spring immediately to mind, how much closer perhaps does it bring us to a partial understanding of the situation that faces whom today, if at all, and what is it?

On my last evening in Yomsof, as I sat playing poker in the Laughing Cossack Saloon, with the mechanical piano tinkling in the background, a bottle of kvass at my elbow, and the rowdy frontiersmen pushing past to get at the Circassian dancing-girls who were doing high kicks in long skirts on a rickety rostrum, I tried to find answers to all these questions—and more, for the kvass was made from bread and cranberries. I wish I could tell you the conclusions I reached, but I fear I cannot. All I can find in my notebook for that evening is a memorandum just decipherable, to the effect that I finished up owing forty roubles to Andrei, who had a remarkable facility for filling a straight flush, and Nikolai's remark as we sat down to play. " Come," he said, drawing his double-edged sword and laying it on the table, " we are all brothers under the skin. You have nothing to lose but your change."

Red Art and the High Jump

THE position of artists, writers and composers in the Soviet Union is by no means enviable. This is due to the fact that their work is constantly being interrupted by conducted troops of intellectual sightseers from the West, who come poking about asking loaded questions about Pasternak and wanting to hear someone hum the piece Shostakovitch once had to compose to celebrate a reafforestation project.

" Some days we can hardly get a stroke of work done," a sculptor called Mikhail Sorobni told me. " They come tramping into our studios with their notebooks and their pitying smiles, and we have to down tools and listen to all that stuff about freedom of expression, and the unfettered genius of Mondrian, and the position of the artist in a civilized society, and what Tolstoy would have said, and how art knows no barriers. It's enough to make you cry."

Sorobni lives in what is variously known as the Chelsea, the Greenwich Village or the Left Bank area of Moscow—a collection of eight-storey blocks of flats specially provided for accredited practitioners of the arts, with studios and all artistic conveniences, a little way out of the centre of the city along Leningrad Chaussee. He assured me that the amount of official red tape he and his fellow-workers in art have to put up with in the colony is negligible. There is no question, for instance, of clocking-in, and Sorobni himself told me of a novelist who at that time had not put pen to paper for three whole days.

" In his weekly progress report to the Controller of Cultural Output he will explain that on Tuesday he was doing research at the Permanent All-Union Construction Exhibition at 74 Fruzenskaya Embankment, checking up on the mechanism of a cement-mixer for his big scene in Chapter Ten; that on Wednesday he was working out a sub-plot in his head; and that on Thursday he just simply didn't seem able to get started, somehow. No questions will be asked. His movements at the Construction Exhibition will of course be investigated, and he may possibly be required to produce an extra five thousand words next week to make up for that blank day on Thursday. Otherwise he will hear no more about it. Could you possibly wish for any less troublesome conditions of work? "

Certainly, as I moved about this bohemian quarter I found no evidence of dissatisfaction. The only hint of real complaint I heard was from a poet, who objected to the system of payment. " We get fourteen roubles a line," he said, " and since I have been detailed to write only sonnets, in iambic penta-meters, I often find it hard to make ends meet. Now Nicholas next door, who never puts more than three words in a line, and usually only one, manages to run a four-seater Moskvich *and* a ZIL with independent suspension. I sometimes think I'd have been better off as a monumental sculptor: at least they get danger money for all statues over nine feet high, and they are allowed to sell their chippings by the sack for gravel paths."

Accommodation in these blocks of artists' flats is arranged so that there is no possibility of confusion. At each main entrance there is a notice-board, giving full details of the occupants and the nature of their work. Thus, outside one block I read:

Floors 6, 7 and 8.—Painters of suspension and cantilever bridges, fire-stations, cranes, hydro-electric plants (by moonlight), sewage-farms, snow-ploughs (post-1953 pattern), coke-ovens and heavy machinery of all kinds except steam-shovels.

Floors 4 and 5.—Painters of clothed female workers, smiling. Sculptors of Stalin (these apartments are to let). Sculptors of People's Artist of the U.S.S.R. Ulanova. Satirical poets (Room 13—visiting hours 1.30 p.m. to 2 p.m.—no files, weapons, tobacco or newspapers to be brought in to the prisoners). Ode writers.

Floor 3.—Canteen.   Writers of novels with eight or more principal characters. Painters of steam-shovels and sunsets over collective farms, with or without figures in the foreground.   Rewriters of history.   Translators and adaptors of Western musical comedies prior to *White Horse Inn*.

Floor 2.—Painters of wholly or partially unclothed female workers (visitors strictly forbidden).   Chaperones' waiting-room.   Office of the M.V.D.

Floor 1.—Crêche. Recreation room.   Painters of murals, processional banners and official notices.   Illustrators of cultural cookery books. Documentary film makers (Uplift Section).   Writers of popular songs.

Ground Floor.—Assorted composers.   Janitor's office.   *Pravda* leaderwriters nearing retirement age.   Artists' Materials Supply Store (all requisitions to be countersigned by the Ministry of Approved Sedentary Recreation). Comical Cartoonists (Bloated Uncle Sam and Child-Eating John Bull Division).

I passed several pleasant evenings among the inhabitants of this gay Quartier Latin, and learned a good deal about their devil-may-care way of life.   In one studio I attended a typical artists' party.   The men were dressed just as casually as artists the world over, in dark-brown or navy-blue serge suits, with brief-cases on their knees and handkerchiefs in their top pockets.   Their shoes were of brown or black leather, and they frequently raised their voices in quite animated conversation over their cups of strong hot tea or domestic sherry.   The ladies were chiefly artists' models, and I need hardly tell you that a certain amount of winking went on, for we all know the abandoned atmosphere of the *vie de Bohème*.   Still, as far as that goes, *honi soit qui mal y pense,* I hope.   One model, after a glass of vodka which some particularly high-spirited playwright had given her, was actually on the point of taking off her hat and overcoat, but fortunately good sense prevailed, and the danger passed without embarrassment.

Still, a lot of the talk was distinctly outspoken, to say the least, and I have no doubt that I might have been shocked more than once if it had not been for my earlier experiences in similar gatherings in the vicinity of King's Road, Chelsea, or Fourth Street, New York. A novelist, for example, told us that he intended to have the hero kiss the heroine *three times* in the space of a single chapter of his next book—and before they were even engaged, at that. " And damn the consequences!" he cried recklessly, his voice ringing above the barbaric sound of the accordion being played in one corner by an Authorised Humorous Essayist wearing an amusingly unconventional necktie. (It was striped.)

" That is the spirit of the true artist, you see," was my host's comment on the novelist's outburst. " Oh, we are regular devils, make no mistake. I admit there have been petty restrictions, especially under Stalin; but we have emerged once again. Art cannot be fettered. Take me. My last painting but one was of a female worker wearing only a pink chemise and bathing a practically naked two-year-old child. As I said at my trial, it was obviously very warm in the room—a tribute to the efficiency of Soviet central-heating. Socialist realism, you see. They saw my point at once, and I got off with a fine of a hundred roubles and the confiscation of the picture. Not the frame, of course. Oh, we are moving with the times, I can tell you. And you can see the results for yourself: we are a breezy, uninhibited crowd, caring not a fig for convention."

At half-past nine the lights, which were controlled by a master switch in the Janitor's office, went out abruptly, and the party broke up. I felt that this was a pity, for we happened to be in the midst of a most rewarding discussion about the influence of Ethel M. Dell on decadent Western novelists of the mid-twentieth century, and a poetess had promised to follow this up with a dramatic reading from her latest work, *Lines Addressed By a Mother to Her Son on the Occasion of His Being Decorated as an Honoured Costing Clerk Second Class With Bar*.

" Perhaps some other time," she exclaimed quietly, as the guests filed out into the long, bare corridor and made their way to their respective cubicles.

Sorobni took my arm.

" I don't want you to get the idea," he said in an urgent whisper, " that we artists of the Soviet Union waste *all* our nights in riotous debauch and mere frivolous pleasure-seeking of the kind you have witnessed to-night. Far from it. If we did, how do you think we could possibly keep up with the Five-Year Plan for Cultural Expansion, under which we have already more than doubled our output of Edifying Post-Revolutionary Industrial-Romance Novels? No, my friend, you can take it from me that we stick as rigidly to the official schedule as any Western artists—possibly more so. As a result, the day is coming when we will outstrip you in this field as we have outstripped you in the fields of space-exploration and the manufacture of sal volatile. We will outstrip you in James Barrie, in Dickens, in Whitman, in Upton Sinclair, in Shelley, and even in Steinbeck. We will outstrip you in *Lolita*."

" Steady on," I said.

" Already Marshak's translations of Shakespeare are acknowledged as more

brilliant than the originals, and so is Bunin's Longfellow. Finally we will outstrip you in Nevil Shute and Edgar Allen Poe—and *then* where will your literary pre-eminence be? "

I also found great activity in theatrical circles in Moscow and Leningrad. There are more than thirty theatres in Moscow alone, and while I was there a few of them were not showing either *The Lower Depths* or *The Seagull*. I asked the reason for this.

" The Russian public likes change," a producer told me. " When a man has seen *Uncle Vanya* a hundred times, say by the age of thirty-five, he tends to look out for something fresh, and so, of course, we have to cater for this restlessness. For instance, at my theatre we have been presenting *Anna Karenina* and *The Cherry Orchard* on alternate weeks for the past eighteen years. Now we have put into rehearsal a production of *Caste,* and it will be added to our repertoire as soon as possible. There will be an outcry, naturally, from the diehards—but there must be progress. Russian youth has a right to learn something about conditions in England to-day, and how better than through the work of your more realistic playwrights? "

" How indeed? " I said. " And what about *Gammer Gurton's Needle?* That should open their eyes a bit."

The position of ballet dancers in the Soviet Union is unique. When a *prima ballerina* gets on a bus (it doesn't happen often) the other passengers rise and take off their hats. If it happens to be a *prima ballerina assoluta,* they tear up their tickets and shower her as with rose petals. If it is Ulanova, the bus is removed from service at the end of the shift, appropriately labelled, and placed in a museum. A ballerina is allowed to go straight to the head of any queue, and she also has the right to hit people with her umbrella if they fail to curtsy. Ballet dancers in training (that is, approximately one-fifth of the population under the age of fourteen) are fed twice a day on honey, strawberry jam, the top of the milk, very thin slices of bread and butter, and a teaspoonful of vintage champagne. They sleep in cotton-wool, and may with impunity make rude signs at any member of the Central Committee they chance to meet. They are not obliged to pay for anything. Their advice is often sought on matters of policy by the Presidium of the Supreme Soviet. Until they have taken their final vows they are immolated in the Bolshoi Theatre, where they practise *Swan Lake* night and day. If they show any signs of developing a technique more advanced than that current in 1910 they are transferred to the nearest fruit-canning plant and deprived of their superannuation. The

men are between six and seven feet tall. I could not find out for certain whether they get extra rations, but I strongly suspect it. They tend to throw the girls much higher than any choreographer could reasonably expect, and they are fond of boasting that they haven't dropped one yet. They suffer from a sense of frustration because in the field of ballet they can find no foreigners to outstrip, and I heard rumours that in desperation they are shortly to start competing with the Japanese in the production of No plays.

Finally, I went into the question of sport, and although I found hard facts and statistics difficult to come by on account of the secrecy with which the Russians surround their activities in this direction, I learned enough to make me very fearful for the future. In the first place I found that spies are continually touring the country, snapping up three-year-old high-jumpers of promise, embryo pole-vaulters, natural born 1,000-metres champions, infants with a strongly developed butterfly stroke, schoolboy light-welterweights, or centre-forwards of genius frittering away their talents in obscure village teams for the fun of it. Such valuable citizens are spirited away in camouflaged trucks at dead of night, for distribution among the various Training Grounds. These are chiefly situated in inaccessible valleys in remote parts of the Union, heavily guarded and out of bounds to all but inspectors from the Ministry of Sports and Pastimes. I heard of baseball pitchers who are being secretly reared on the great plains of the Ukraine in preparation for the day when the Moscow Redshanks, having exercised their right to enter the World Series, humble the New York Giants into retiring from the game and switching to competitive backgammon. Cricketers are being coached behind closed doors in Kuibyshev and Ulanovsk, and already there are rumours of batting averages that would make an English Test captain shake in his pads. There is a well-drilled squad of Cossacks in Stavropol which is expected to be ready to provide jockeys capable of filling the first fourteen places in the Grand National by 1970, many of them riding bare-back and at least one hanging under the belly of his horse playing " The Song of the Volga Boatmen " on the concertina as he approaches Valentine's Brook the second time round. In the wildest part of the Yakut A.S.S.R. I myself managed to stumble by accident into a Tennis Compound and what I saw was frightening. There in a deep natural cave extending for three-quarters of a mile into the side of a mountain, hundreds of players of both sexes were grimly practising high forehand volleys by numbers. Electric lights were strung along the roof of the cave, and in small recesses first-aid workers waited to attend to cases of exhaustion, hysterics, or

blistered feet. The sounds of thudding tennis balls, the words of command, the grunts of exertion, the cracking of whips and the snapping of racket strings echoed from wall to wall in the most eerie fashion, and the memory of the place haunted me for weeks. I met no Russians who were aware of its existence, but one woman in Kiev, whose daughter had gone out to play with her bat and ball one evening a month before, and never come back, asked me piteously whether I had noticed a little girl there with red bloomers and a cast in one eye.

"I'm afraid not," I said. "But I've no doubt that's where she'll be, and I shouldn't worry a bit. One of these days she'll turn up at Wimbledon and beat the living daylights out of all those Australians, and you'll be the proudest mother in Russia."

"If I thought it would end there," she said, "I might be able to sleep at nights. But sometimes I wonder: when we have outstripped *everybody*, what will remain for us to do?"

"I'm very glad you asked that question," I said.

The Bosom of The Family

TO sum up, then.

The U.S.S.R. is a land of boundless opportunity—a vast empire whose backward subject nations are not yet ready for the great adventure of self-government but who are moving, one is tempted to hope, more or less in that direction. It is the cradle of Gorki and Pushkin; the refuge of Maclean; the home of the concealed microphone, lamb cutlets served on daggers and the Scriabin Museum: where H is pronounced en but with the tip of the tongue against the teeth, where spring lasts only two weeks, and where *Fromage Soviètique* costs 5/3d. a portion. It is also the last remaining stronghold of Communism, and it occupies nearly a seventh of the land area of the planet Earth, which nevertheless manages to revolve around the Sun in an ellipse while simultaneously rotating about its own axis. How long this happy if somewhat cumbersome state of affairs can be expected to continue is anybody's guess, and I remain sanguine.* Mr. Oblov, a Moscow man in the bosom of whose family I stayed for a while, assured me that Mr. Khrushchev has no plans for any large-scale tinkering with the solar system as at present

* Somebody must.

77

constituted, such as adjusting the inclination of the Earth's axis to the plane of the ecliptic in such a way as to deprive Lincolnshire of sunshine during the month of August, or arranging for three-eyed saboteurs from Venus to land in Iowa and poison the potato crop; and Mr. Oblov struck me as having his finger pretty well on the pulse of things, with the ear of the Secretary of State for Tarmacadam and access to many of the little confidential notes that circulate among the Council of Ministers.*

But I will be telling you about Oblov later. Meanwhile I must try to get down as many as possible of the multitudinous sights and sounds and impressions that remain with me of the fabulous U.S.S.R. before I am escorted out of this chilly waiting-room at Moscow Airport with a coat over my head and forced into the waiting aeroplane. It stands there now, out on the fog-haunted runway, its great engines turning, ready to whisk me back to the gentle delights of democracy, capitalism, licensing laws, Whitechapel Road in the pouring rain, and the blessed freedom to do just whatever I like in the certain knowledge that somebody, somewhere, is going to make a profit out of it.

So many memories come crowding back. Once again I am standing in awe, surrounded by breathless sightseers from all parts of the world, before the railings that fence off the Summer Garden in Leningrad from the River Neva. Nowhere have I seen such railings. It is not for nothing that Leningrad, quite apart from its reputation as the Venice of Russia, has been revered by railing-fanciers down the centuries for the sombre beauty of its wrought-iron spikes, the grandeur of its quietly rusting cross-ties, uprights and decorative blobs.

Ah, but there is more to Russia than railings. I shall remember too how I was reminded of Blackpool or Coney Island as I watched the laughing crowds of holiday-makers strolling along the Lenin Embankment in Yalta, with their open-necked boiler-suits, their ice-cream cones, and their saucy little cardboard hats bearing such legends as Какая тёплая погода!† or Есть—ли у вас английские папиросы?‡. I shall remember long, lazy afternoons on the beaches of the Black Sea Coast, where the workers come to claim their allotted weeks of rest—for this is the sanatorium belt: here on the Russian Riviera, instead of financiers, apprentice film-stars and the elegant riff-raff of international yacht society, you meet humble textile workers with nervous

---

* An example of these, which he showed to me one day, was addressed to M., and read: " Comrade Anya is an Honoured Copy-typist, and it is no part of her duty to drink vodka with you half the afternoon behind the filing-cabinets in Room 71a. Please submit full report.—K."

† What warm weather! ‡ Have you any English cigarettes?

debility, certified by their foreman and at least one doctor as being due for a few days' paddling and the regulation dose of State-controlled vitamins. This fashionably pasty-faced group here, for instance, disporting themselves with a beach ball, wearing calf-length shorts and arch-support open-toed sandals— they are not, as you might be forgiven for thinking, some titled racehorse-owner with his cabaret-artist wife, his company-director son and his debutante daughters: they are operatives from the sand-blasting department in a cup and saucer factory in Smolensk, down here to recover from cut fingers, nasty coughs or dyspepsia. All through the blazing days of summer the work-worn toilers come and go, building up reserves of energy so that they can earn better marks for Attention to Duty, Increased Output and Smartness on Parade. All is free: knife, fork and spoon, railway vouchers, spa treatment, Swedish drill, food allocations, boat-trips to Balaklava, and admission to the Old-Tyme Dancing on the end of the pier. I think I have never seen a more contented lot of holiday-makers.

" Mind you," one of them told me as we strolled along the prom to attend a lecture on the History of the Steam Hammer in the flower-decked band-stand, " there are times when you feel like screaming."

" And what do you do about that? " I asked.

" No provision has been made for it," he said with a shrug. " We await the issue of a directive. In the meantime, between you and me, one screams as quietly as possible, in the privacy of one's wardrobe or some small cupboard."

I shall remember the enormous mosaic panel entitled " Abundance " in the Vladimirskaya Station in Leningrad; the site of the original Garden of Eden at Sukhumi in Abkhazia, where guided excursions pour in and out of the Medical and Biological Research Centre to look at the monkeys; the tea plantations and Australian dragon trees in Batumi; Sunzhunskoye Lake with its 180 acres of health-giving mud; the lovely walk through the park from the Balneological Institute to the Lenin Health Centre in the Dendrarium at Sochi; the Vorontsov Palace in Alupka, designed by Edward Blore and built in green malachite with lead instead of mortar; Tatar villages of white-washed houses clinging to precipitous mountain sides, fragrant with the scent of roses in the evening air; the Ostankino Estate Museum of Serf Art at 5, Pervaya Ostankinskaya, Moscow; the Frunze Central Park of the Soviet Army at 2, Commune Square in the same city—not to mention the Underground Print-shop of the Central Committee of the Russian Social-Democratic Labour Party (Bolsheviks) 1905—1906, at 55, Lesnaya Street, or the Central Theatre of Transport at 8a, Kazakov Street. I shall remember the saddles encrusted with sapphires in the Moscow Kremlin Museum—and the jackboots of Peter the Great, the chain armour of Alexander Nevsky's father, Catherine's clock with a gold bird on top dropping a diamond from its beak every second, the biggest topaz in the world, the jewelled Easter eggs containing platinum railway trains, the horse-blankets made of parrot-skins, the thrones, crowns, sceptres, mitres, robes, jewelled guns—all the glittering riches of Czar and Church displayed to relieve the boredom of Muscovites on rainy afternoons. I shall remember dun crowds of simple Russians waiting in queues to file rever-ently past the embalmed remains of Lenin and Stalin, who between them managed to kill off more simple Russians than any Czar would have believed possible.

But most of all I shall probably remember my stay with the Oblovs. They were introduced to me, after a long battle with Intourist and the Ministry of Official Secrets, as a Typical Russian Family. The Soviet Government has a number of such families on its books, for display purposes: indeed, I under-stand that *all* governments make a point of keeping a few Typical Families on hand, in case of unexpected visits by foreign diplomats or other busybodies who might wish to pop in to some humble dwelling for a cup of tea and a chat with a typical housewife about how quickly kiddies wear out their typical shoes.

The Oblovs, I was told, were about as Typical as a Family could be without being downright ridiculous. It was unfortunate, the Intourist people said, that I could not be introduced instead to the Smirdayevs, who were if anything just a shade less typical but had the advantage of a plug which perfectly fitted their bath (a rare thing in Russia, for some obscure technological reason). However, the Smirdayevs were fully booked for the next three weeks, what with English Members of Parliament and a honeymoon couple from Peking, and I must make do with the Oblovs. As things turned out I was delighted. Constantin Oblov, a temporary civil servant of about forty-five, took me in at once and insisted that I should live as one of the family. When I demurred at this, pointing out that I was not actually used to sleeping in a three-tier bunk on the landing, he arranged that I should have the iron bedstead, a prized possession dating back to the time of Rasputin; and so the bargain was sealed: in exchange for my last remaining camera, three black market tickets for the Bolshoi and an old envelope autographed on the back by four members of the Aston Villa football team, I was to share the Oblovs' lives until a week the following Monday—or until his newly married daughter moved in to occupy the spare half of the kitchen with her husband and their two dogs, whichever was the sooner.

Oblov was a short, squat man with a chubby face and two suits that always looked as though he'd slept in them, although he assured me he never did.* He was full of fun. On Saturday nights it was his custom to get reeling drunk with some of his pals from the department, and come home intent on setting fire to the block of flats. How we laughed on that first Saturday night, as he blundered about the living-room like a bear, knocking ikons off the wall and burning himself on the stove in his attempts to take off his snow-shoes! " We want only peace! " he kept on shouting, as his wife, Elyena, grappled with him and his young daughter, Vera, tried to get the militia on the tele- phone. Elyena was also short and squat, and if it comes to that so was Vera, who was learning to be an oxy-acetylene welder. The only member of the family who wasn't short and squat was Constantin's grandfather, a peasant of ninety-seven from the wilds of Georgia, who hated the rush and sophistication of life in Moscow and spent most of his time in a communal outhouse at the

---

* I asked him point blank, for it is only by hard-hitting question and answer that we can ever hope to learn the truth about life behind the Iron Curtain.

back of the flats, pouring strong beer on to red hot stones to make an alcoholic vapour bath. At other times he sang the songs of his youth and tried to puzzle out the jokes in *Krokodil*.

Elyena worked in the Metro, at the awe-inspiring Taganskaya Station, where six and a half pounds of pure gold were used in the decoration of thirty-two Wedgwood blue porcelain bas-reliefs depicting the Russian armed forces, and when she got home in the evenings she was pretty well dead beat. Still, the samovar was always on the boil, and if Constantin arrived first he would quickly spread the tablecloth and get out the pickled herrings, smoked sausages, bread and butter, kvass, juicy melons, tinned beans, roly-poly pudding, vinogradny sok,* sour cucumbers, plum cake, caviar, cold roast mutton, or whatever was going. I found Russian food quite palatable, and I was interested to see that for the most part it is eaten with a knife and fork, or sometimes (as with soup) with a spoon. Fish is eaten with fish eaters. Chocolates are eaten straight from the silver paper. Shchi (a pickled soup made from fermented cabbage) is quite often left on the plate—although, as Elyena kept telling the baby, it is very good for you: many people in the world today, she explained, as for instance the squads of ravenous hobos who live on moss and raw thrushes on the Epsom Downs, would be glad of the chance of a spoonful any day. Occasionally, for a treat, Elyena would cook us some kissell, which is a jelly made from cranberry juice and sugar thickened with potato flour. And once she took us for a picnic to the Park of Culture and Rest for Railway Workers, where the engine-drivers, ticket-collectors and firemen made a soothing picture, lying about on grassy banks with their boots off and their tunic buttons undone, reading Turgenev and listening to snatches of Tchaikovsky. I remember thinking, as we washed down our sardine sandwiches with vodka, that British Railways are singularly lacking in initiative in some directions.

The Oblovs' son, Nikolai, was eighteen, and was doing very well for himself as an atom scientist, junior grade. " It's an overcrowded profession," his mother told me, " but what can you do? At any rate, he passes all his exams with flying colours, and he never eats sweets or goes out with girls. He'll be worth a small fortune in a few years, with his own troika and a dacha and his photo in *Pravda,* and perhaps even some decent false teeth." Young Vera, on the other hand, was something of a problem. Her heart did not seem to be in her oxy-acetylene welding. She told me herself that she would secretly

---

* Tomato juice.

like to go to Wolverhampton or Hampstead and be a beatnik. She loved the hot singing of Rudy Vallee. She wore beads and showed her knees, which were short and squat. Many a night she was out until half-past nine, whooping it up at the ice-cream parlour on the corner with her disreputable friends. '' They put lipstick on their cheeks,'' her mother told me, '' and the boys get their hair cut like Vice-president Nixon. One Friday night Vera came home here with a book written in English by Elinor Glyn, and for the rest of the week-end she sat on our sheepskin rug in her liberty bodice, eating grapes. Sometimes I wonder where it will all end. We want only peace, God knows, but this seems a terrible price to pay.''

Ah, Elyena, I shall think of you often in the years to come! And of you, too, Constantin—and little Vera, and Nikolai—and you, old puzzled grandfather trying to find your way in a strange new world. For you showed me the real Russia during the days I spent among you. I shall think of the velvet curtains in your sitting-room, the well-thumbed *Baptist Messenger* on the red plush sofa, the snow on the window-sill, the lace doilies, the aspidistra, the stuffed birds under glass. I shall hear again your humdrum problems—your hopes, your fears, your plans, your joys, your disappointments—so typical, so familiar . . . How often, as we sat quietly watching the Cossacks on your television set (what comical fellows they were, to be sure!), with the baby snoring in his crib and Constantin dozing over the racing results in the evening paper—how often did I imagine myself to be in some humble dwelling in Balham, or Peoria, or Bootle, or S.W.3! For you were real, and your lives were real, and our talk was of all the trivial things that truly matter. Whereas these men who take my arm now and lead me to the waiting 'plane out there on the dim-lit runway, they are not real—any more than the men who tapped my telephone calls throughout the length and breadth of the Soviet Union, or spied on me in shops and restaurants and intercontinental ballistic missile research establishments, or went through my luggage, or opened my letters, or treated me as a dangerous enemy for the simple reason that they *must have* a dangerous enemy even to be at peace with, or their world will collapse about their ears . . .

On the other hand, of course, now that I come to think of it, you and your whole family might easily have been a put-up job.

Not that I'm at all suspicious by nature, you understand. But I can see I must think this over very seriously during the long flight home. After all, a traveller returning from a foreign land must be very careful how he makes his report.

Postscript

NATURALLY enough, I have had to answer a lot of questions since I got back from the U.S.S.R. I do not complain about this, because I know how fascinating and mysterious the place must seem to the ordinary man in the street who just doesn't happen to be enterprising enough to pack a few things and go and see for himself, instead of pestering the life out of me. Just the same, it can get tedious.

The enquiries have ranged from the romantic or sentimental (" Are there any burlesque shows in Leningrad? ") to the downright offensive (" Where the hell did you get the money? "), and in order to save myself any further inconvenience (if there's one thing I detest it's being buttonholed on my way into a restaurant on a wet afternoon and asked how long it takes to get from

Sukhumi to Tiflis), I have decided to set down here a definitive List of Questions and Answers on Russia. If your own particular pet query is not among them you must either (a) ask somebody else, or (b) take it that there is in fact no such question.* I think I have covered most of the ground, though.

For security reasons I have deliberately avoided giving such information as the exact number of men in the Russian armed forces at the time of going to press, or the average monthly expense account earnings of a member of the Presidium; but to balance this I have gone out of my way to answer one or two questions which nobody has ever even asked me, and if that isn't service I don't know what is. Here we go, then.

Q.—Is the Russian language difficult?

A.—Yes. If it comes to that, so is the Ukrainian.

Q.—Did you get the impression that enough was being done in the matter of cultural exchanges between the U.S.S.R. and the West, or too much?

A.—I have devoted a good deal of serious thought to this subject (without, I might add, so much as a thank you), and I am convinced that the Russians must be provided with more of our TV. Westerns, life-subscriptions to *Variety,* inexpensive reproductions of paintings from Dali's middle period, mixed bundles of books from the *Forever Amber* school, lampshades with liqueur labels on them, introductions to cafe-society, facilities for the syndication of two-colour comic strips, Mr. Edward R. Murrow or a reasonable facsimile, translations of the works of Kerouac and Sax Rohmer, and handy pocket guides to Disneyland. Otherwise I don't see how we can win. It's no good *telling* them that the capitalist system is worthwhile: we've got to *prove* it. As far as the East-to-West part of the cultural traffic is concerned, I don't know how you're fixed but I haven't even got round to finishing *Dr. Zhivago* yet.

Q.—How long *does* it take to get from Sukhumi to Tiflis?

A.—Nine hours by train. Why?

Q.—Would I find the Russians hospitable?

A.—Hard to say offhand. They might hate the very sight of you. You strike me as the type who keeps jumping to his feet all the time, shouting " When does a fellow get anything to eat in this house? " Normally, though, you'll find that they live up to the old Russian proverb, *It won't*

---

* Vaguely in this connection it is interesting to note that among ordinary Russians today there are more answers than questions. Latest figures show that the proportion is about six to five, but the gap is narrowing.

cost you a kopeck. A Russian will offer to give you the very coat off his back, if the question of people giving away coats happens to crop up. In that way he's just like you. Also, just like you, he'll sulk for a week if the offer is accepted. In Georgia hospitality is carried to extraordinary lengths. In the courtyard in front of his house, the average Georgian keeps a large vat sunk in the earth. When a stranger arrives— I'm not speaking now of rag-and-bone men, meter-readers or escaped convicts, but *bona fide* strangers who look as though they might do the same for you one day—he is welcomed with a pitcher of delicious cool wine ladled out of the vat as he crosses the threshold. This happened to me on quite a number of occasions. The last time, I remember, I also had several pitchers indoors before I left, and on my way out, what with one thing and another, I fell into the vat. " Well, really," my host said as he grumpily threw me a rope, " I must say this is stretching hospitality to its limits." They dried my clothes, though.

Q.—If I tried *very hard* do you think I could get a working knowledge of Russian in a month?

A.—No. Try me on Ukrainian.

Q.—How about Ukrainian?

A.—Not a chance.

Q.—Is the world going to be blown to smithereens?

A.—Do you mind? I think this gentleman was here before you.

Q.—What should I take with me on a trip to Russia?

A.—That's more like it. Well, now. Those little wire brushes for cleaning suede shoes are always handy, don't you think? How about a few snaps of the wife and kiddies? Or some spare torch batteries? The field is pretty well wide open, really. I took a lot of paperclips myself, and a thing for opening tea-chests, and a propelling pencil that would write in green, red and black, but I didn't find much use for any of them. You can never tell, can you? As a matter of fact, now that I think of it, I decided to leave the pencil at home at the last minute, and for all I know it might have proved invaluable. Here are a few basic tips, if you're really worried:—

You can get eggs in Russia.

Don't have too many brown-paper parcels in your luggage. What kind of people do you want them to think we are?

Take plenty of string, if you like, but don't bother about manganese.

Russia contains 90 per cent of all the manganese there is.

Any opium or elks' horns you may have with you will be confiscated at the customs.

Q.—When was Tbilisi pillaged and burnt to the ground by the Persians for the last time?

A.—1795.

Q.—*Why* is the Russian language so difficult?

A.—I'm getting just about sick and tired of you.

Q.—Who are " The Volga Boatmen? "

A.—Some people in a painting by Ilya Yefimovich Repin.

Q.—From what you learned in Russia, are you disturbed by the news of their latest achievements with long-range rockets?

A.—I am disturbed by *all* news. It so happens, though, that I met the chap who turns out most of these rockets, and he told me in confidence that they are more of a sideline, really. " What I'm much more interested in," he said, " is developing a really comfortable space-ship so that a couple of our boys will one day be able to travel to Venus and bring it back here for close scrutiny." " The space-ship? " I said. " No," he said. " Venus." I asked him whether his rockets should meanwhile be regarded as a menace in the West. " Good heavens, no," he said: "they're not even loaded. Besides, the more rockets *we* have, and the more rockets *you* have, the more we'll both be able to disarm, thus releasing men for work in the factories." " The rocket factories? " I said. " Have some more caviar," he said.

Q.—Who wrote the incidental music for *Macbeth* by William Shakespeare?

A.—Aram Khatchaturian.

Q.—Shall I be able to get decent medical treatment?

A.—Well, I never saw any witch-doctors. As a matter of fact health is highly regarded in the U.S.S.R., and much sought after. People often live to be a hundred and fifty, especially in Azerbaijan.

Q.—How do you account for that, then?

A.—You keep out of this. One of the chief centres of health is the resort at Sochi-Matzesta, the jewel of the Russian Riviera. If you keep your eyes open in the Matzesta Valley or Khosta you'll see a lot of prospectors and geologists drilling for sulphureous-hydrogen medicinal water. The Russians can't get enough of it. For all I know you may suffer from circulatory ailments, diseases of the joints, high blood-pressure, scalp

infections and sinus trouble. If so, this is the stuff you want. At Matzesta they'll pour it into you, boil you in it, spray you with it, and give you a few bottles to take home for the medicine-chest. It will also turn a silver coin black in forty seconds flat.

Q.—On the 21st of June, 1898, Konstantin Stanislavsky and a man called Nemirovich-Danchenko began a discussion in the Slavyansky Hotel at No. 17, October 25th Street, Moscow. The discussion lasted twenty-four hours. What the devil were they talking about all that time?

A.—You're just trying to catch me out, aren't you? They were discussing the possibility of inventing Marlon Brando, Tennessee Williams, Anton Chekhov and Marilyn Monroe. By the time they came out they had formed the Moscow Art Theatre. " Well," Danchenko said, as they slipped into the nearest dram-shop, " it's a start, anyway."

Q.—Do you suppose there'll be another war?

A.—Just a quick one.

Q.—What struck you as being the most pleasing feature of life in Moscow?

A.—The fact that the Russians are sufficiently grown-up not to permit continuous performances in their cinemas. You go into the Forum, the Metropol, the Salut, the Khudozhestvenny or the Stereokino at the time stated on your ticket, like a civilised person, and you never find yourself having to watch Ivan laboriously cuddling Natasha when you've already seen her pushing him over a cliff in the last reel and go streaking off to Samarkand with Boris.

Q.—You were saying about the Russian language . . .?

A.—I have nothing more to add, but if you insist I don't mind letting you into a few secrets. As a matter of fact I don't think you'll find Russian absolutely impossible, so long as you have a working knowledge of one or more of the sister languages—Polish, Bulgarian, Serbian or Czech. The whole business was tidied up considerably after the Revolution, when the Soviet authorities, looking round desperately for things to abolish, cut a lot of redundant letters out of the alphabet and laughed like the very devil. Those letters haven't been heard since, except in whispers, but some of the ones that remain are enough to frighten the life out of you. There are nine vowels, some hard and some soft, and twenty consonants—including an R written back to front and pronounced " Yah." H is N, P is R, and E is pronounced " Ye " as in the English " Yes," except when there are two dots over it, when it is pronounced " Yo " as in the English " Yogh." No, I don't know how to pronounce " Yogh," but I can easily find out for you. Meanwhile, a thing like an apple with two stalks sounds like F, and the sound expressed by our letter W does not exist at all for Russians, which must be a grievous loss. They use the letter B instead, only it sounds like V, and that accounts for the fact that they tend to speak English with a foreign accent. Russian grammar, too, is full of interest. To begin with, there are exceptions to all rules, but I wouldn't count on it. It is also important to bear in mind that you are likely to meet a few expressions where, instead of the genitive case indicating a small quantity of divisible matter (as Maximilian Fourman of Kiev University has so aptly put it), a masculine noun has the dative. You'll just have to be philosophical about this, I'm afraid, and if the worst comes to the worst you can always point, or make signs. Days and months have no capitals. " Day " is masculine, " Night " is feminine, " Morning " is neuter.

Q.—Why?

POSTSCRIPT

A.—Let's have one question at a time, please. There are reciprocal verbs and reflexive verbs, but no sign of a continuous present. Apart from Nominative, Vocative and all the old familiar cases, there is an Instrumental Case and a Prepositional Case. On the other hand, there is no possessive pronoun for the third person—a point which was greatly appreciated by the Marxist planners. Finally, here is some phonetic Russian for you to learn by heart. It might help or it might not, but in any case you'll find it just the thing for parties when you get back.

Phonetic Russian	*Plain English*
Ya Amerikanka.	I am an American woman.
Zdrastvooite. Ya Angleechahnin.	Hello. I am an Englishman.
Kharoshaw.	Good.
Khasasho lee vwee spahlee?	Did you sleep well?
Mwee khateem as matret gorod, spaseeba.	We want to see the town, thank you.
Vwee zahftrakalee?	Have you had breakfast?
Da.	Yes.
Skolka stoeet, pazhalsta?	How much does it cost, please?
Cheteerysta.	Four hundred.
Ya khachoo spat.	I want to go to bed.
Prasteete?	I beg your pardon?
Eezveeneete, eta glahvnaya ooleetsa?	Excuse me, is this the main street?
Mozhet bweet.	Perhaps.
Parah fstavaht.	It's time to get up.

Q.—Don't you know any more?

A.—Nyet.

Index

About the Authors

Alex Atkinson was born in Liverpool in 1916. Originally a shoe salesman, a soldier (from 1940-1946), and a repertory actor, he is the author of a play and three novels. *Exit Charlie,* his most recent novel, was published in America in 1956. Among his hobbies are "the theatre, Beethoven, worrying, and lying down." He has been a contributor to *Punch* since 1948 and made his mark as a foreign reporter when he successfully crossed America by rocking chair in 1959.

Ronald Searle was born in Cambridge, England, in 1920. A Japanese prisoner of war in Siam and Malaya from 1942 to 1945, he became a cartoonist after the war for the *Sunday Express* and *News Chronicle,* eventually joining the staff of *Punch* in 1956. He makes his home in London with his wife, Kaye Webb, and twin children. He is a Director of Perpetua Books.

Mr. Atkinson and Mr. Searle have collaborated previously on *The Big City* and *By Rocking Chair Across America.* Mr. Searle is also known in America for his witty illustrations to such books as *Paris Sketchbook* (with text by his wife) and *The Anger of Achilles,* Robert Graves' new translation of *The Iliad.*